ROLLS-ROYCE HERITAGE TRUST

ROLLS-ROYCE
and the
MUSTANG

David Birch

HISTORICAL SERIES No 9

Published in 1987 by the
Rolls-Royce Heritage Trust
PO Box 31 Derby England

© 1987 D Birch

Reprinted with amendments 1997

This book, or any parts thereof,
must not be reproduced in any form without the
written permission of the publisher

ISBN 0 9511710 0 3

Cover: AL963, the fourth mustang to be converted to take the Merlin 65. Seen here it features the dorsal extension to the fin, later removed and replaced by an increase to the chord giving an additional 3 sq ft of area. The photograph was taken at Duxford where the aircraft was under evaluation by the Air Fighting Development Unit. (Photo. Cliff Glidewell).

Printed by Bemrose Security Printing, Derby

CONTENTS

FOREWORD

David Birch has been researching and writing on matters of aviation history, and in particular on aspects of the work of the Rolls-Royce Experimental Flight Test Establishment at Hucknall for more than twenty years. His interests in aviation first developed at the age of seven and shortly after leaving school, he became an apprentice Coppersmith with Rolls-Royce at Hucknall in 1955. Working on the site gave him the opportunity to meet and befriend many of the engineers and some of the test pilots, both past and present, from whom a great deal of his knowledge and much of his enthusiasm was gained. He was also able to track down much of the aircraft and engine documentation of years ago which had lain discarded in odd corners of the site.

I first came to know David as a superb source of information relative to the Company's flight test activities in the early 1960s. It was not, however, until 1967 when I was appointed to a post at Hucknall that we came to know each other as friends - a relationship which has strengthened in the years which have followed.

Many an hour was spent together during the years when I was privileged to work at Hucknall. We talked and planned on what might be done to conserve the Company's history, to record the work of Hucknall and the story of the Merlin. But time was short and the climate was not then right to engender a general interest in the Company's heritage.

It was during this period that David first started to write about Hucknall and his articles were published by Air-Britain. On three separate occasions he was the recipient of that organisation's Air Writer's Trophy for the most meritorious article of the year.

Flight development ceased at Hucknall following the events of 4 February 1971, and flight testing has since been centred on Filton in Bristol. David did all he could once that decision had been taken to collect and make safe all the archival papers which still existed at Hucknall. These covered, albeit with many frustrating omissions, virtually the whole period of the site's flight test activities from the mid 1930s to 1971.

In due course, David decided to renew his contact with aircraft and their operation and this he sought through applying for a staff post in Product Support. In 1979 he was appointed a Customer Support Engineer on the RB211 and transferred to Derby. Within a year the thought of what was to become the Rolls-Royce Heritage Trust was being actively discussed and David and I shared the satisfaction of helping to see the idea we had discussed many years earlier come to fruition.

David researches, compiles and edits the Archive magazine of the Derby branch single handed, serves on the Branch committee and takes responsibility for all the archives amassed by the Branch.

This book on the Mustang had its origin in an article David wrote for Air-Britain in 1970. In recent years a massive amount of dogged research has been put into compiling this book, which represents the definitive story of the conversion of the Mustang to the Merlin engine. With the Merlin, the Mustang became one of the most outstanding fighters of the war years. This is the story of how that came to be.

Mike Evans
Chairman, Rolls-Royce Heritage Trust

5

Acknowledgements

It is now well over forty years since the events related in this book took place and most of the great names, and I might add characters, concerned with the story are no longer with us. Thankfully, Rolls-Royce plc still retains a vast amount of documentary material from this era and the author is grateful to that company for the access allowed him to the archives of the Technical Library. I am also indebted to the Photographic and Graphic Illustrations departments for their preparation of photographs and artwork. A snippet of information here and there over the years all helped, not only to add to my knowledge but to create a kind of ambience, or insight, about what it was like in those days. Such a regression is an enormous benefit to the historian who, in this case, was only three years old when the Merlin Mustang first flew!

To the undermentioned names and organisations I am very grateful for the help, however large or small, that they have given me during the preparation of this book. Not everyone was able to supply relevant information, but in fairness to all I would like to extend my gratitude to those who steered me in other directions and in doing so enabled me to make new friends. Such eagerness was particularly forthcoming from the mother country of the Mustang where fellow aviation buffs responded with much enthusiasm, thus continuing, in effect, the Anglo-American relationship that the Mustang fostered all those years ago. There is no doubt that the Mustang provokes as much enthusiasm with the present generation as it did with the last. Long may it do so.

From Rolls-Royce, Hilda Allsobrook, Alec Harvey-Bailey, Lucille Desmond, Glen Dickson, Barbara Dilks, Ian Edlin, Mike Evans, Richard Haigh, Ronnie Harker, Stan Hart, Peter Kirk, Brian McCune, T D Sills, John Staton, Gordon Weir, and the Hucknall and Derby Photographic Departments: Ken Osborne of Rolls-Royce Inc: Brian Dorey: Paul Coggan of Mustang International: June Carmichael and A Williams of the Imperial War Museum: Joan Fisher of Associated Press: Gordon Swanborough of Air International: B C Kervell of the Royal Aircraft Establishment Museum at Farnborough: The Aircraft and Armament Experimental Establishment Library at Boscombe Down: Miss Parks of the Air Historical Branch: Graham Stanley of the Public Record Office: From the United States, Norman Avery: Alex T Burton: Jeffrey Ethell: Cliff Glidewell: William R Lewis: Paul Ludwig: John Morgan: the late Edgar Schmued: John Sullivan: Walter J Boyne of the Smithsonian Institute: M Sgt Roger A Jernigan of the Office of Air Force History at Bolling AFB: Earl Blount, Mike Matthews and Curtis E Ruckdaschel of Rockwell/North American. And finally, my thanks to the girls who put it all onto the word processor, Liz Theobald and Monica Anderson.

Crown-copyright material from the Public Record Office is reproduced by permission of the Controller of Her Majesty's Stationery Office. All such information used in this book is taken from PRO files AVIA 8/754, AVIA 15/1717 and AVIA 46/132. The reports reproduced in Appendix III and IV are also Crown-copyright as are the photographs of AM208 at Boscombe Down and that of Sir Wilfrid Freeman. The photograph of Lt Col Thomas Hitchcock is Associated Press copyright. All other photographs and illustrations, unless otherwise stated, are the copyright of Rolls-Royce plc.

Bibliography

Development of Aircraft Engines and Fuels: Schlaifer and Heron, published by Harvard Univ., 1950.

Mustang - The Story of the P-51 Fighter: Robert W Gruenhagen, published by Arco, 1976.

Mustang - A Documentary History: Jeffrey Ethell, published by Janes, 1981

INTRODUCTION

Few will argue that the North American Mustang powered by the Rolls-Royce Merlin engine was America's finest all-round combat aircraft of the Second World War. Specified and ordered in 1940 by the British Air Purchasing Commission during its search for suitable American aircraft to supplement the types then in service with the Royal Air Force, it was produced in the remarkably short time of 120 days. Unfortunately, its low-rated Allison engine was incapable of permitting the airframe's advanced aerodynamic features to be exploited to the full with the result that the RAF relegated it to close-support duties and the Spitfire still reigned supreme in the medium and high altitude fighter roles.

This story is about the rebirth of the Mustang and the role played by Rolls-Royce in that event. The greatest part by far was played the Company's Experimental Flight Test Establishment at Hucknall in Nottinghamshire. Parented by Derby, yet completely autonomous with the means of installation design, development and manufacture, it was a unique organisation among aero-engine manufacturers.

During the telling of the story much use has been made of contemporary memoranda associated with the project and in most cases these are reproduced at the appropriate juncture in the story. In some cases these writings, apart from referring to a specific point of issue, also give information on other contemporary matters. Where these matters can be considered in some way relevant to the story or reveal an attitude of a party involved, or if they are just simply interesting or amusing, they have been left undisturbed. Irrelevant paragraphs have been omitted as have the writers' names. The latter is revealed in the document reference at its heading and can be deciphered by referring to the table explaining the Rolls-Royce reference system. If nothing else the correspondence reveals the close relationship that existed between Rolls-Royce, the Air Staff and other parties during those critical times.

The reproduction of such documents has it drawbacks in that the names of various personalities consistently crop up without reference to their title or role in the events. To avoid interfering with the flow of the text I have resorted to footnotes to provide identification. Most of what will be read has been obtained from Company archival material though occasional use has been made of other sources in order to portray a wider view of events. Unfortunately, the search for contemporary American records on the subject has not been so successful. This story is, therefore, one-sided. Thankfully, perhaps, it is the more important side whereupon everything was happening and some information is contained therein to give the reader an insight into American attitudes towards the project.

These were the paramount years in the Company's history and no other civilian aeronautical organisation could field a first-eleven to match the likes of Hives, Elliott, Lovesey, Hooker, Rubbra and Lappin, along with Hucknall's Dorey, Hart, Challier, Harker and Shepherd. Willoughby 'Bill' Lappin, Hives' personal assistant, who divided his time between the Nightingale Road factory and the Company's London office in Conduit Street, plays a major part in the story being the link man between the Company and the Air Ministry, Royal Air Force, North American Aviation, the American Embassy and the U.S, Army Air Force. He knew everybody that mattered and they knew him.

This publication also enables the opportunity to be taken to reveal the story behind Rolls-Royce's unsuccessful attempt to produce an aircraft to its own design based on certain Mustang features. Strange that in the middle of a war which was demanding all of the Company's resources in producing and developing an established range of engines, along with new designs, it should embark upon a project so radical. The decision was more remarkable when one considers that Hucknall had been established a mere eight years earlier by engine-minded men. During those eight years a great deal of experience with airframes had been accrued throughout the design and installation of power-plants and the necessary structural alterations involved, so much so that by the end of 1942 the draughtsmen and stressmen felt confident in taking on the production of an indigenous design. That they didn't entirely succeed was not their fault - nothing changes faster than technology during a war.

ROLLS-ROYCE AND THE MUSTANG

Conception to conversion

The history of aviation is peppered with instances of technical innovations brought about as a result of chance. The right person with the right idea being at the right place at the right time. The marriage of the Merlin engine to the Mustang airframe was such an example.

The story begins with a phone call from Wing Commander Ian Campbell-Orde, Commanding Officer of the Air Fighting Development Unit (AFDU) at Duxford, to Ronnie Harker, Rolls-Royce service-liaison pilot. It was Harker's job to fly aircraft in service with the RAF units and Air Ministry establishments in an evaluation or troubleshooting capacity. He was no stranger to Duxford where his job had taken him on a number of occasions to find out how the Merlin was performing in service and to give advice where needed. It was also his brief to fly aircraft powered by engines of the Company's competitors, British and American, and German if the chance arose.

Campbell-Orde informed him that one of the new Allison-engined Mustangs had arrived at Duxford and offered him the opportunity to fly it. Harker had no hesitation in accepting for although he had heard the usual reports of remarkable performances that often heralded a new American fighter, this one appeared to be living up to its reputation. However, scepticism lingered as Hucknall had had some previous experience with the Allison V1710 engine and in its view the performance, particularly at altitude, left much to be desired.[1]

Deciding to make a day of it Harker hired a car from the local garage in Hucknall and in the company of his wife, Marjory, and a fuel systems engineer named Stowe set out for Duxford. It was 30 April 1942. On arrival he flew AG422 for thirty minutes and was very impressed. Its manoeuvrability and speed were excellent and the performance at its fighting altitude, 10,000 to 20,000 feet, was most commendable although the low-rated Allison provided little above this height. Clearly, the Mustang's airframe was very advanced and possessed all the virtues of aerodynamic cleanliness. The next day Harker issued his report.

To Sg and Hs.   Sft/Hkr.1/IW 1.5.42.

c to Dor.
   Lov.
   Lp.   SECRET
   Dor/Chr.

FLIGHT TEST ON MUSTANG

A 'Mustang' single seat fighter made by the North American Aeroplane Co. has been on test at the A.F.D.U. at Duxford.

---

[1] During 1940/41 three Curtiss Tomahawks were test flown at Hucknall for performance calibration, investigation into cutting-out, vibration tests and troubleshooting the cause of generator drive failures.

Mustang 1 AG422 at the Air Fighting Development Unit at Duxford - the aircraft that started it all. It was this aircraft that Ronnie Harker flew on 30 April 1942 and as a result recommended that the Merlin engine should be installed in a Mustang. (Photograph Crown Copyright).

> I have read their report on it.........I flew the aircraft yesterday and can bear out many of these points.
>
> This aircraft should prove itself a formidable low and mid-altitude fighter. It closely resembles an Me.109F, probably due to its being designed by one of the Messerschmitt designers, who is now with the North American Aeroplane Co.[2]
>
> The point which strikes me is that with a powerful and good engine like the Merlin 61, its performance should be outstanding, as it is 35 m.p.h. faster than a Spitfire V at roughly the same power.

The nomination of the Merlin 61 was a wise choice. At the beginning of the year Hucknall had re-engined AB197, a standard Spitfire Vc, with the new two-speed, two-stage supercharged Merlin LXI (as it was then known) developing over 1500 bhp, thus converting it into one of the prototype Spitfire IXs. This modification had given it a new top speed of 417 mph, an increase of 44 mph, at 28,000 ft. Harker's prophetic final sentence and a visit to Duxford by Willoughby Lappin *(Lp)* resulted in serious interest being taken in the proposal.

---

[2] Edgar Schmued was the man who led the Mustang design team and though he hailed from Germany he never worked for Messerschmitt.

10

To:- Dor.   Lp./JL 4.5.42.

I saw the Mustang at Duxford yesterday and I see in Hkr's report about his visit that he claims it to be 30 m.p.h. faster at 5,000' and 35 m.p.h. at 15,000' than a Spitfire V.

The aircraft itself is certainly very clean indeed, but we do not consider that there is this superiority of performance of the Mustang over the Spitfire V.c.

Whilst the figures in regard to performance etc. from the A.F.D.U. should occasionally be accepted with some reserve, in actual fact the Mustang at Boscombe is given the top speed of 354 at 10,000', 370 at 15,000' and 361 at 20,000, the total weight of the aircraft is 8,652 lb.

I would like to talk to you about this machine sometime.

Harker did not let the grass grow under his feet and had gained the support of Ray Dorey *(Dor)*, Manager at Hucknall, who in turn encouraged him to go direct to Hives *(Hs)*. Pointing out the virtues of a Merlin-powered Mustang he suggested that Hucknall should be allocated an aircraft for conversion. Harker recalled the meeting with *Hs*. After listening to what he had to say *Hs*, obviously won over by what he had just been told, reached for the telephone and before long had Sir Wilfrid Freeman, Vice Chief of the Air Staff on the other end. This was typical of Hives, never one to waste time once his mind had been made up. The details were related to Sir Wilfrid with the recommendation that Hucknall should be allocated an aircraft for conversion. There then took place the first official meeting between Rolls-Royce and the Ministry about the Mustang.

SECRET

Hs.   Lp2/LA.14.5.42.

Re: Mustang.

I had lunch yesterday with D.C.A.S.,[3] and A.C.A.S.[4]

At a meeting yesterday on a very high level, it was suggested to the Minister that the LXI should be tried in the above machine, so you may hear about this, but if not you could put it on your list of points for next meeting with C.R.D.

I feel myself that it might pay a very good dividend, if it can be done quickly, to install the Merlin XX in this machine. It would be a relatively quick job, and might fill a very useful interim niche under existing conditions. I am endeavouring to obtain performance data about the aircraft so that the gain that might be anticipated can be estimated. I recall that Mansell[5] and Jones[6], Boscombe, when in U.S.A., did suggest that the Packard should be fitted into the Mustang aircraft, but it did not get any further.

Both D.C.A.S., and A.C.A.S. stressed to me the urgency of the Spitfire IX, and I pointed out that we were doing everything in our power on this

---

[3] Deputy Chief of the Air Staff, Air Vice-Marshal N H Bottomley CBE CIE DSO AFC.
[4] Assistant Chief of the Air Staff, probably Air Vice-Marshal R H Peck CB OBE (ACAS General) or Air Vice-Marshal R S Sorley OBE DSC DFC (ACAS Technical Requirements).
[5] Air Commodore R B Mansell CBE, Commandant of the Aeroplane and Armament Experimental Establishment (A&AEE) at Boscombe Down.
[6] E T Jones OBE, Chief Superintendant A&AEE.

job, and also tactfully indicated that they were very fortunate in as much as we had both the will and the capacity to undertake what we had done. They also both supported the interim Griffon versions of the Spitfire and Typhoon, and again stressed the importance of the final aircraft being equipped with the Griffon LXI.

Re getting jerk on Griffon Spitfire, I had decided to call and see Major Kilner[7] at Weybridge on this job, but on giving the matter second thoughts considered it might be more politic, at least at this stage, to see Commander Bird[8], and this I propose to do tomorrow if he is available. Smith[9] himself is very worried about the whole fighter situation, and he is anxious for our support in getting something moving.

Plainly, the Ministry had some misgivings about the proposal, not unnaturally so as they were about to put into service the Spitfire IX in an effort to combat the latest German threat, the Fw190. This mark of Spitfire had been ordered in quantity and any new venture that threatened the supply of Merlin 61 engines would not engender a great deal of enthusiasm with the Air Staff. To a certain extent Lappin also shared this view. Whilst the Company was confident that it could provide enough Merlin 61s to supply the Spitfire production lines, more so when American production of the engine was eventually underway, it nevertheless felt obliged to hedge its bets by offering the Merlin XX as an option.

With the proposal now beginning to simmer the time had arrived for the gas to be turned up. What was now needed was a set of accurate performance curves which would show not only the top speed and rate of climb figures for the Merlin Mustang but its superiority over other types of aircraft. To this end Lappin wrote to Dorey.

To: Dor.   Lp.4/JL. 19.5.42.

I enclose herewith the American flight test report on the Mustang single seater fighter with Allison engine, and a very excellent document it is.

A very brief use of a slide rule would appear to indicate that the machine is going very much faster than a Spitfire for less power, and we shall be glad if you will kindly ask Chr. to let us have:-

1. A curve for the Spitfire V.

2. Performance curve for the aircraft, fitted with standard Merlin XX., and possibly the 46 showing the standard performance plus the emergency boost figure.

3. Similar data for the Merlin 61 with the estimated increase of weight involved in either case.

4. Your own comments as to how long it might take to install either engine.

I would point out that the report quotes a speed figure of 386 m.p.h. at 15,500', Boscombe I believe have given 370 m.p.h., but I understand from a report of N.A.A. that this has gone up to 378 m.p.h., so I think the mean between the top and low figure should be used by Chr.

---

[7] Major H P Kilner, Managing Director of the aviation division of Vickers Armstrongs.
[8] Squadron Commander James Bird OBE FRAeS MINA RNAS (Rtd), Special Director of Vickers Armstrongs and one-time owner of Supermarine.
[9] Joe Smith FRAeS AMIAE, Chief Designer at Vickers Supermarine.

12

I also enclose a copy of their Flight Manual Report which is also very complete.

To assist in this exercise Mustang AG518 was sent to Hucknall from Speke[10] on 29 May for a series of trials to evaluate thoroughly the performance of the aircraft in its standard configuration. The Aircraft and Armament Experimental Establishment (A&AEE) at Boscombe Down had previously undertaken a similar evaluation and their findings were also sent to Hucknall. Hucknall's performance engineer, Polish exile Witold Challier *(Chr)* set to work. Meanwhile, enthusiasm for the project became contagious and quickly infected the inhabitants of 1 Grosvenor Square, London W.1.

Dor . . . . from Lp.   Lp.9/CP 3.6.42.

Hs. has no doubt told you about the up-to-date position in regard to the Mustang and every effort is being made to locate Wincott[11] and if he is being held up waiting for a seat on the other side instructions will be given to take the data from him and send it in the first aircraft leaving.

The Americans are red hot on this proposal now and Mr. Winant[12] has given certain instructions to the Air Corps.

Apropos Mustang, we want some curves which refer to Mustang only so could one of your people reproduce three sets of three sheets each setting forth the estimated performance of the Mustang in colour :

1. A performance comparison of American Mustang and your Hucknall performance.

2. The estimated speed performance of the aircraft with Merlin 20 and Merlin 61 as per last curves.

3. The estimated climb performance of the same aircraft at the appropriate weights.

We do not want the Spitfire to appear on these curves as they will probably go to America via the American Embassy.

Hs . . . . from Lp.   Lp.11/CP 3.6.42.

Mustang

C.R.D.[13] agrees installation 61 proceed, subject to stress figures being satisfactory.

Every effort is being made to locate Wincott and the data on the other side to get it over here at the earliest possible moment.

Bouchelle[14] has seen C.R.D. and he afterwards saw the Ambassador who, I understand, has cabled instructions to General Arnold[15] to arrange for the installation of a Packard Merlin in the machine immediately and to give 'Priority 1' in the factory.

Bouchelle has given an approximate date of four weeks.

---

[10] Lockheed Aircraft Services at Speke Liverpool, assembly plant for Lend-Lease aircraft from the USA.
[11] Group Captain C B Wincott, British Air Mission, Washington.
[12] John G Winant, American Ambassador to Britain.
[13] Controller for Research and Development, MAP, Air Marshal F J Linnell CB OBE.
[14] L B Bouchelle, North American Aviation representative.
[15] General H H Arnold, Commander of the United States Army Air Forces.

ESTIMATED SPEED PERFORMANCE

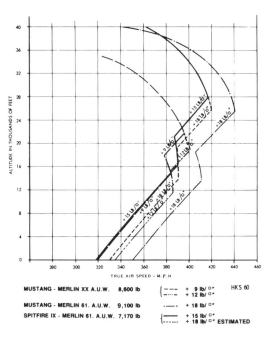

MUSTANG - MERLIN XX A.U.W.   8,600 lb   { ---   + 9 lb/ □"   HKS 60
                                              { --·--   + 12 lb/ □"

MUSTANG - MERLIN 61. A.U.W.   9,100 lb   --·--   + 18 lb/ □"

SPITFIRE IX - MERLIN 61. A.U.W.   7,170 lb   { ——   + 15 lb/ □"
                                              { ------   + 18 lb/ □"   ESTIMATED

Challier's performance curves in which the knowledge he had of the Mustang's aerodynamic qualities, weight and dimensions were allied with the power of the Merlin. Seasoned with ejector exhaust thrust, propellor diameter and efficiency, and the correct reduction gear ratio, air intake efficiency and percentage of charge intercooling, he came up with one of aviation's best recipes. The estimate shown above was his first attempt drawn up during the first week of June 1942. In MS gear the sea level speed was 345 mph rising to 410 mph at the FTH of 13,800 feet. With the power diminishing with height the speed dropped off accordingly, but only by a few mph up to the changeover at 18,500 feet. At this altitude the supercharger automatically kicked into high gear (FS), full rated boost was restored and speed increased until at 25,600 feet the maximum of 441 mph was attained. Despite the subsequent fall off in power 400 mph was still attainable at 36,000 feet. These results were calibrated in accordance with the gear ratios of the high altitude Merlin 61. With the subsequent decision to go for the lower altitude Merlin 65 and from the results of the performance tests on Hucknall's Allison powered aircraft they were amended to give a top speed of 432 mph. In the event Challier was spot on.

These memos are interesting as they show that there was strong American interest right from the decision to go ahead with an initial conversion. The Packard Merlin referred to was the V1650-1 American version of the Merlin XX then being produced for the Curtiss P-40 and for Lancasters and Hurricanes as the Merlin 28.

Challier's report was issued on 8 June. It gave a top speed of the Merlin XX version as 400 mph at 18,600 ft, but the speed with the Merlin 61 installed had leapt phenomenally to 441 mph at 25,600 ft.

POWER REQUIRED IN LEVEL FLIGHT

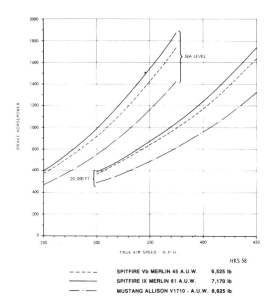

HKS 58

- - - - -	SPITFIRE Vb MERLIN 45 A.U.W.	6,525 lb
—————	SPITFIRE IX MERLIN 61 A.U.W.	7,170 lb
— · —	MUSTANG ALLISON V1710 - A.U.W. 8,625 lb	

If proof were needed that the Mustang's aerodynamic qualities were the reason for its superiority over contemporary fighters then this graph says it all. At sea level the Allison Mustang required 480 bhp to enable it to fly at 250 mph whereas its equivalent, the Merlin 45 powered Spitfire V which was 25% lighter in weight, required an additional 100 bhp. At 350 mph the difference had widened to 260 bhp and at 20,000 feet it was still in the order of 200 bhp. For the Allison Mustang to achieve the 430 mph top speed of its Merlin counterpart its engine would have to produce just short of 1200 bhp. The Mustang X, however, was 500 lb heavier and its Merlin 65 produced an additional 200 bhp in order to achieve this figure. The graph, therefore, is only representative of the three types of aircraft depicted.

Graph HKS 58 shows the amount of power required for a particular airspeed in level flight at sea level and 20,000 feet. It shows quite conclusively that the Mustang airframe, despite being heavier, produced far less drag than either the Spitfire V and IX, to such an extent that when all three are compared at the Mustang's top speed of around 375 mph, the latter's engine was producing around 200 bhp less at 20,000 feet. What is equally obvious is that the faster it flew the greater became the power-required margin.

On 9 June the Drawing Office took charge of AG518 for one week for Stan Hart and his team to determine how they were going to install the Merlin.

The month of June also saw a dramatic rise in correspondence on the subject, mainly between Rolls-Royce, the American Embassy, North American Aviation and the Air Ministry.

To Dor. from Hs.   Hs.22/KW 9.6.42.

The Minister of Aircraft Production[16] rang me up last night to say that he had seen the American Ambassador who had promised him that they would have a Merlin 28 flying in a Mustang in the U.S.A. in a month's time.

He wanted to know whether we could not beat the American time. I told him that we could not have a machine flying in a month, but we were still willing to have a gamble that we should be flying before the Americans.

As soon as possible, we should like the probable date of completion of the Mustang. There is no doubt that considerable interest is being taken in this machine and the R.A.F. will require all they can get for next year.

Lp.7/JL   9th June, 42.

Wing Commander I.R.Campbell-Orde,
Air Fighting Development Unit,
Royal Air Force Station,
Duxford,
Cambs.

My dear Campbell-Orde,

Thank you very much for the Mustang and Me.109F reports. I am now trying to get a picture in my mind of the general fighting situation, in order that we can try and frame our own policy and line up some of the other factions which appear to be floundering about.

We have two Mustangs now at Hucknall, and for your unofficial information we hope to install a 61 in one of these aircraft. I do not think there is any doubt that we shall get the Americans interested on their side of the water, in using, perhaps some Packard Merlins in the same machine.

Lp.1/LA   11th June 1942

Air Marshal Sir Wilfred Freeman,
V.C.A.S.,
Air Ministry,
King Charles Street,
Whitehall, S.W.1.

Dear Sir Wilfred,

I enclose some preliminary figures as a result of our investigations of the Mustang.

The loose sheet in the folder will show you the powers available, and the first sheet in the folder is the really interesting one as it gives you a very good assessment of the drag, and clearly indicates that this American aircraft has a very low drag for which, so far, there is no very definite explanation.

The performance figures for the aircraft, you will note, are based between the low figure obtained at Boscombe Down, and the high figure quoted by N.A.A. We have since done performance tests on the aircraft, and as a result the figures quoted on these curves may be reduced by 2%.

---

[16] Colonel J J Llewellyn PC CBE MC TD MA.

The Allison installation. The identity of the aircraft cannot be positively ascertained but as the photograph was taken in June 1942 odds are that it is either AG518 or AM121, both of which were employed on preliminary performance investigation prior to conversion. Note the sealing of the gun ports and the elbow feeding the downdraught carburettor. Compare with similar photograph of Merlin 65 installation.

Retrospectively, it is now very evident that we should be in a much better position today had your instructions some years ago to one of the aircraft firms building fighters, been put into effect.

Lp.1/LA   12th June 1942

Major Thomas Hitchcock,
The American Embassy,
1, Grosvenor Square,
London, W.1.

Dear Major Hitchcock.

I was very glad to learn from Bouchelle about the progress being made in regard to the project for the Mustang with Packard Merlin, etc.

We on our side are pursuing the matter with intensive energy, and I would like to take this opportunity of saying how much I appreciate your efforts and congratulate you on the results, which I hope in due course will pay a good dividend for our joint war effort.

Lp.6/JL   16th June 1942

Air Marshall Sir.W.Freeman,
V.C.A.S.
Air Ministry,
King Charles Street,
Whitehall,
London. S.W.1.

Dear Sir Wilfred,

I hope you were interested in the Mustang performance figures which
I sent to your office last week. We have since made a further exploration
into this and we think it is not unlikely that we can again improve the
performance by improved blowers and reducing the supercharger ratio.

However, my real reason for writing you was to say that Group Captain
Wincott is now in this country for three weeks, and I feel sure you would
much appreciate an interview.

Lp.1/JL   17th June 1942

Group Captain P.W.S.Bulman,
British Air Commission,
1785, Massachusetts Avenue,
Washington, D.C.,
U.S.A.

My dear George,

Wincott turned up alright last week-end and I picked him up on Monday
morning and brought him to Hucknall......... I hesitate to say much on
paper about things as they are here, except to express our admiration for
the 'Mustang', and note with a little astonishment that it goes so quickly.
We are, as you will have no doubt learnt by now, taking an extremely
energetic interest in this machine and hope that it will pay a good dividend.

It was most interesting to have a talk with Winkie about the general
situation, and I can now understand that you had rather a tough job in
U.S.A., but I am sure, and it is even now very evident, that is has been
well worth while and you are to be congratulated for some of the stuff
that is now beginning to make its appearance.

Hs.7/KW   17th June, 1942.

Air Chief Marshall Sir W.R. Freeman,
V.C.A.S.,
Air Ministry,
King Charles Street, S.W.1.

Dear Sir Wilfred,

I view with alarm the fighter position for next year. I do not think there
is a hope of Supermarines keeping their promise on the Griffon Spitfire,
and as the complete prototype machine has not yet flown, it will be a
miracle if it goes through without numerous essential aircraft mods.

We have insisted on a meeting at M.A.P. with the Minister, which takes
place on Friday afternoon, Supermarines and ourselves being present; but
of course a meeting at the M.A.P. does not produce any aeroplanes!

In order to anticipate the fighter position next year we are arranging to commence deliveries of Griffon 61's in March instead of August/September, but I do not think there are going to be any aeroplanes.

The best bet at the moment is the Mustang. We have now got it agreed that we shall convert three machines instead of one. We are cleared on the stressing and the c.g. of the machine; the schemes are completed, and the drawings are being issued to the shops.

Somebody has got to make sure that there is a good supply of Mustang airframes.

Another variation we are looking into is that for a super low-altitude fighter the Mustang will take the Griffon II-B engine. We have not got the final figures for this, but I mentioned it as an indication that you cannot get too many of those machines.

The risk of course is that if we make the Mustang into a first-class machine the U.S. Army Air Corps will want to collar them, because the information we have had from the U.S.A. is that their fighter position is by no means clear

Lp.18/JL   23rd June 1942.

Major Hitchcock,
American Embassy,
London.

Dear Major Hitchcock,

I would like to say how pleased we were to have you visit us here yesterday and Mr. Hives has written to General Lyon[17] suggesting that he pays us a visit one day next week.

Apropos the additional Mustang for U.S.A., I confirm that Mr. Hives will personally take this matter up with Air Marshall Linnell.

Lp.20/JL.   23rd June 1942.

— Legarra Esq.,
North American Aircraft Ltd.,
St.John's House,
Smith's Square,
London.

Dear Mr. Leggara,

First of all I hope I have spelt your name correctly.

I am not sure whether Mr.Bouchelle has left yet, but I believe I did promise to let him have a sample of our Pilot's Notes which we prepare for issue to the boys who are flying the aircraft. I enclose these two samples herewith, dealing with the Merlin XII in the Spitfire II's and the Merlin XX and XXI used in the Hurricane.

We had Major Hitchcock up yesterday, who was able to see for himself the little progress we have made in regard to the 'Mustang', and if at any

---

[17] Brigadier General A J Lyon, Air Technical Section, US Army Air Corps. Technical officer of the Air Corps in Britain. He died suddenly at about the time that the prototype American conversion made its first flight.

time you wish to discuss matters affecting the policy of this aircraft if you will let me know we can arrange to meet. The whole matter seems to have boiled up very nicely, and it would appear to me that the machine has a very bright future.

NORTH AMERICAN AVIATION, INC.

INGLEWOOD   CALIFORNIA

ST. JOHN'S HOUSE,
SMITH SQUARE,
LONDON, S. W. 1.

W. Lappin, Esq.,   26th June, 1942.
Messrs. Rolls-Royce Limited,
D E R B Y

Dear Mr. Lappin,

You did spell my name correctly.

Thank you very much for the Pilots' Notes on your 2 Engines; Bouchelle has already left for the States, but I will forward them on to him.

I called in at Hucknall on Wednesday of this week, and am very pleased with the progress that has been made. However, there is bound to be a certain amount of trouble in such an installation, and the major one at present seems to be the Fuel System, - but I am sure that can be taken care of.

We have been receiving many enquiries about this proposed installation, and I agree with you that the airplane will have a very bright future.

Yours sincerely,

P. H. LEGARRA
NORTH AMERICAN AVIATION, INC.

Hs.6/DK.   28th June, 1942

Air Chief Marshall Sir W.R. Freeman,
V.C.A.S.
Air Ministry,
King Charles Street,
London S.W.1.

Dear Sir Wilfred,

We feel very depressed about the fighter position, both in this country and the U.S.A. and this has not improved since one of our own pilots examined the F.W.190. The Spitfire 8 and 9 will make a big improvement and we are also developing another version of the '61', which will give its maximum performance at a lower altitude.

The aircraft manufacturer, however, has got to make some contribution. So far, since the war started the entire improvements to the fighter performance have been due to engines and airscrews.

We are sold completely on the Mustang. The Merlin 61 goes into it with no alteration to the engine cowling or to the radiator cowling.

We are pressing forward with the conversion of these machines, but as hundreds of small detail drawings have to be produced, special radiators, etc, it will be towards the end of August before it is flying.

We have asked that 250 sets of conversion parts shall be put in hand, and have pointed out that if this is agreed to it will save at least three months in getting the machine into service and we will undertake the work at Hucknall.

We are now running a Griffon 61 on test and are very pleased with it. It is the best fighter engine in the world, but there will be no aeroplane for it. In spite of us delivering the first Griffon engine to Supermarines last November, their first machine, which can only be considered a 'mock up', because it has been flying with the standard Spitfire wings, has only completed 22 hours in the air. The first machine with the correct wings is not yet flying, so the prospects of getting this machine operational for next year will demand nothing less than a miracle to happen.

One would feel more comfortable if the Typhoon was in a better position, either with the Sabre or the Centaurus.

SECRET

My dear Hives,   30th June, 1942.

Like you I feel worried both about the fighter position and the fact that the aircraft designers are not helping to achieve technical and tactical superiority over the enemy.

It is proved over and over again that technical superiority confers an almost overwhelming advantage on its possessor. The Battle of Britain and the Libyan operations are outstanding examples.

I agree with you that 250 conversion sets should be put in hand, but why only 250? In the old days we should have chanced our arms. Anyway I will do what I can to get an order for 500 sets put through to-day.

Can you convert 6 Mustangs instead of 3? I should like to send no less than 2 to U.S.A.

Finally, we must get the North American Company to go absolutely full out on a super Mustang with the Griffon 61, so as to get the best of both aircraft design and engine design with backing at the highest level and unstinted help in the way of drawing office staff and jig and tool makers, we might beat all records for getting a new aircraft developed and into production.

Although it is 'against the rules', come and see me soon.

Yours sincerely,

W.R. Freeman.

Lp.13/JL.   30th June, 1942.

Captain R.N. Liptrott,
Ministry of Aircraft Production.
A.D.R.D.T.l.,
Millbank,
London S.W.1.

My dear Liptrott,

Many thanks for your long and excellent explanatory letter of the 24th inst. concerning the Mustang performance.

First of all I would like to say that we are, above all people anxious to avoid shooting a line about aircraft performances with our engines, and are only anxious to contribute in some measure to the production of a final aeroplane which in the hands of the Fighter boys will beat the Germans. Therefore, our official at Hucknall who does our performance projections does make an honest attempt to arrive at the right answer, but I have never known anything which has so many variants in regard to getting at the final and absolute figures as the present day aeroplane.

I agree with you about the Mustang and why the performance is so good, when I saw the aircraft first I did not believe it, but a closer inspection clearly indicated that it was externally quite clean very well made and the standard of workmanship and finish I believe would result in a very good average high figure being obtained from the production machines. Your figure for the Mustang with the Merlin 61 is about 12 m.p.h. down on ours, but even if this proves to be correct it still is a very good aeroplane as far as speed is concerned. In any case we are working full throttle at Hucknall and will convert three aircraft to take the '61' engine and we aim at having the first one finished possibly by the end of August.

Six weeks after issuing his first report Challier revised his figures in the light of the performance tests carried out on AG518. It had also been decided that a new propeller would be constructed for the Merlin Mustang with a diameter of 11 feet 4 inches and a reduction gear ratio of .42:1 driving it. This would replace the previously proposed Spitfire type of 10 feet 9 inches with a gear ratio of .477:1. The final performance estimates of both the Merlin XX and 61 versions were:-

	MERLIN XX	MERLIN 61
All up weight	8600 lb	9100 lb
Max speed at sea level	331 mph in MS[18]	345 mph in MS
Max speed at F.T.H	393 mph in FS[18] at 18,600 ft	432 mph in FS at 25,500 ft
Absolute ceiling	37,100 ft	40,800 ft
Operational ceiling	32,700 ft	37,200 ft
Service ceiling	36,300 ft	40,100 ft
Rate of climb	2360 fpm	2480 fpm
Change to FS gear at	14,800 ft	18,400 ft

The first aircraft earmarked for conversion was AG518, but on inspection it was found not to be up to the latest production standard,[19] weighing only 7530 lb due to lack of armour, guns and wireless equipment. Its successor was AM121 which arrived on 7 June 1942 and was immediately employed on performance investigation tests. Weighing 8620 lb and being 8 mph slower at 371 mph, it replaced the former which by now had been withdrawn from flying to enable the design staff to study how the Merlin was going to be fitted. Although the Merlin 61 had been the chosen engine from the beginning, fingers were crossed in hope that a new version of the engine offering the same performance at a lower altitude would be ready in time for the first flight. This engine was the Merlin 65.

---

[18] See Appendix VI.

[19] The original production batch was maker's model NA-73. The first variation was the NA-83 which featured various modifications to enhance its operational capabilities. These included armour plating, a new radiator and modified duct, improved rudder trim etc.

Lov.11/JS   24th June 1942.

Major G.P. Bulman
Ministry of Aircraft Production,
MILLBANK, S.W.1.

Dear sir,

With reference to your telephone enquiry this morning, in conjunction with the revised supercharger ratios for the improved performance Merlin 61 blower, the following points were discussed with D.T.D.[20] during his visit to Derby on June 10th.

Modifications to the Merlin 61 blower by increasing the diameter of the first stage rotor and changes in the rotating guide vane and diffuser have resulted in increasing the full throttle height by approximately 2,000 ft., at the expense of a small reduction of the h.p. at the present all-out boost pressure of 15 lb/sq.in. This blower improvement could, therefore, be used for increasing aircraft performance above the full throttle heights, or by adjustments of the supercharger gear ratios could be used for obtaining a substantial improvement in performance below the full throttle heights, while maintaining the present standard Merlin 61 power at full throttle.

At the suggestion of D.T.D. we put in the design of revised supercharger ratios for this improved blower which in conjunction with an increase of the all-out level boost pressure from 15 to 18 lb. will give a static full throttle altitude in F.S. gear of 17,500 ft. and 1540 B.H.P. with a corresponding M.S. gear altitude of 6,500 ft. and 1700 B.H.P. The effect on aircraft performance, for example the Spitfire, would be to give a very substantial gain in speed at 21,000 ft., which is the altitude at which the Spitfire with the standard Merlin 61 changes from M.S. to F.S. Similarly, a further substantial gain in performance would be obtained on the M.S. from sea level up to 10,000 ft. altitude.

It should be appreciated that this development of the improved blower and modified ratios will not be available or in production for some considerable time, and we have yet to make the first sets of experimental gear and carry out the necessary testing.

We have, however, supplied Hucknall with an experimental Merlin 61 featuring the improved blower using the Merlin 60 M.S. ratio, which should give a full throttle height in flight of approximately 8,000 ft. It is intended to fly this engine in the Hucknall Spitfire which will enable us to obtain a performance figure on the envelope curve for the improved blower, and so check up on our performance estimates for the revised gear ratio. We will keep you closely informed of the progress of this development.[21]

A further improvement was the substitution of a Bendix-Stromberg fuel injector in place of the float-type carburettor, the former being preferred for its freedom from cutting-out under negative-G conditions. One of the most important lessons that had been learned during the air battles with the Luftwaffe over Europe and the Middle East was that the days of the float-controlled

---

[20] Director of Technical Development, MAP, N E Rowe CEng FIMechE BSc(Eng) DIC.
[21] This engine, Merlin 61 No.721, had an MS gear ratio of 5.52:1 instead of 6.39:1. It first flew in Spitfire IX AB501 on 3 June 1942. The first stage rotor was 12 inches in diameter instead of 11.5 inches. Various other mods were incorporated in the supercharger and its drive. No worthwhile results were obtained as a bearing failure, necessitating a forced landing at RAF Syerston, occurred after only four hours flying.

carburettor were numbered. The Spitfire and Hurricane were equipped with the standard SU make of carburettor in which, when the nose of the aircraft was pushed down violently, the fuel and the float controlling its level were forced by negative-G to the top of the float chamber. This caused the engine to cut out as a result of fuel starvation or weak mixture due to the jet wells being exposed. The float would then 'float' downwards on the head of fuel accompanying it at the top of the chamber and a second cut-out, this time through being over-rich, would occur. Tests in conjunction with the Royal Aircraft Establishment revealed that the initial cut-out was very brief, perhaps only half a second, but the second one persisted as long as negative-G conditions were maintained.

Irrespective of whether you were chasing the enemy or he was chasing you, this was the last thing you wanted to happen. During the Battle of Britain pilots alleviated the severity of the cut-out by restoring neutral or positive-G as quickly as possible and more often than not it was reduced to a mere fluff, but the advantage still lay with the enemy. The Bendix instrument overcame this problem by injecting the fuel into the eye of the supercharger rotor. It was also less susceptible to icing problems.

Over in Detroit preparations were in hand to produce the Americanised version of the Merlin 61 at Packard. Two years previously Rolls-Royce had sent three of its prominent engineers there to supervise the adaption and production of the Merlin. The most eminent of the trio was James Ellor and in July 1942 details of the changes necessary to convert the high altitude Merlin 61 into the medium-low Merlin 65 were sent to him in order that American engines should be so configured from the start. In the event Packard produced the V1650-3 which was the near equivalent of the Merlin 61. The low altitude version, the V1650-7, equivalent to the Merlin 66, came later.

To. Lr.

Proposed Modifications to the Merlin 61 Supercharger and Bendix Carburettor

Since the Merlin 61 was put into production supercharger development has led to several modifications which have resulted in an improved performance.

It seems possible that these modifications might be standardised from the start in America and full details are therefore attached for your information. Briefly the modifications consist of the adoption of thin vane diffusers in place of the existing wedge vane type, modified circular arc rotating guide vanes on both stages, and an increase in the first stage rotor diameter from 11.5 ins. to 12.0 ins. The effect on the engine performance is shown in two ways (a) by plotting observed supercharger compression ratio against tip speed and (b) by comparing the deduced altitude performance to the two types of engine. You will note that we show an increase of 2,500 ft. in full throttle height for F.S. gear. This is accompanied by a slight drop in constant boost power caused by the increased tip speed, but the full throttle points are on entirely different and higher envelope curve. Comparative characteristics for the two types of supercharger are also attached for your information together with photograph and drawings of the modified parts.

These modifications have not yet gone into production here, but flight tests are at present in progress at Hucknall on both Spitfire and Wellington. No report has yet been issued on the performance of either aircraft, but the results will be forwarded to you as soon as possible.

Regarding the carburettor, it would appear that the S.U.[22] type A.V.T. 44 which is used as standard in this country would not be available in the U.S.A. and particulars are attached of the modifications which have been made to the Bendix No.8 unit to make it function satisfactorily.

We would point out that had No.9 units been available we would have used these and anticipate that less modification would then have been necessary. In their absence it was necessary to develop the No.8 unit and you will note that satisfactory flight tests have now been made to 35,000 ft. on the Wellington without trouble.

As a further development of the improved supercharger a set of revised supercharger gears are now being made up (5.78:1 and 7.06:1 instead of 6.39 and 8.03). These lower gear ratios are being made up particularly to suit the N.A.A. "Mustang" and coupled with the improved supercharger and an increase in all- out level boost pressure from 15 to 18 lb/sq.in. the estimated performance of the engine gives maximum power ratings as follows:-

M.S. 1700 B.H.P/3000 R.P.M./ 6,500 ft.
F.S. 1550 B.H.P/3000 R.P.M./17,500 ft.

These altitudes refer to static conditions (without ram) and in flight become approximately 10,000 ft. and 21,500 ft. The intention is to improve the low altitude performance of the aircraft as much as possible.

As the month drew to a close the second and third aircraft allocated for conversion were delivered. At this time it had been decided that only three aircraft would be converted. For a while these two aircraft, AL963 and AL975, were engaged upon performance and handling trials which was customary in order to ascertain an accurate assessment of each aircraft's individual performance for comparison with that following conversion. AL963 completed a total of 4 hr 15 min flying with the Allison installed whilst AL975 achieved 4 hr 25 min, its final flight before conversion taking place on 2 July. They were then handed over to the Installation Design Dept to assist in the preparation of the necessary drawings, and the following month they were committed to the workshops.

Minute 18 - File SB 38115

To D.T.D   1 July 42

I had a discussion this morning with General Lyon and Major Hitchcock, US Army Air Corps, as to the quickest method of proving the Mustang/ Merlin 61.

My feeling is that if we await acceptance in the States, at best we are going to waste time, and at the worst may find that we are trying to sell an idea which is not favourably received by strong vested interests.

We, therefore, agreed that a good way out would be to let the US Army Air Corps Fighter Force Commander in the UK co-operate on the trials of the Mustang / Merlin 61 as soon as we possibly can. With this in view, I invited General Lyon to arrange for a small contingent to be attached to Boscombe Down as soon as our first preliminary trials were out of the

---

[22] Skinner's Union, the carburettor division of Morris Motors.

way. I also offered to hand over to General Spaatz (the US Air Force Commander) two Mustang/Merlin 61's for trial in the squadrons which will by that time be operating in the UK under his command.

To give effect to this, I want D.T.D to approach Mr Hives at once to know whether a further two, making five in all, Mustangs, can be taken in hand at Hucknall and what will be the price as regards setback of Spitfire IX conversions.

F.J. Linnell C.R.D

(Hives reported that they could take an additional two conversions with minimal disruption to Spitfire IX production. - Author)

To C.R.D   2 July 42

Following discussions this morning before receipt of Minute 18, I advised Mr Hives that his assumption that a Mustang fuselage with Merlin 61 radiators etc installed might be sent to America about October was likely to be replaced by another arrangement.

N.E. Rowe D.T.D

To: Lov/Brns.   Sg.14/DK.2.7.42.

re: The Mustang.

Referring to my recent conversation with you, would you please let me know what is happening about getting a contract for the installation of Merlin 61 engines and how many machines you are trying to get it for.

At M.A.P. on Tuesday, the Minister agreed that we should receive instructions to prepare the parts to complete 500 Mustangs, and make the necessary tools.

Sg.
c. Dor.   Lov/Brns.2/WI. 5.7.42.

re: The Mustang. (Sg.14/DK.2.7.42).

Mr.Foord AD/RDE.2 stated yesterday that he will raise a contract (C.R.D) for the Merlin 61 installation and conversion of three Mustangs, which are to be used for C.R.D. development.

The 500 Mustangs will be an M.A.P. production supply. I have passed your memo. on to Dor. in order that Hucknall may put the necessary arrangements in hand for D.of.E. or D.A.P. contract cover.

To :- Sg.
c.to Dor.   Hs.Brns.4/GW. 10.7.42.

re - Mustang.

Further to memo. Lov/Brns.2/WI. 5.7.42., Mr. Foord has confirmed to-day that 5 instead of 3 Mustangs are to be converted for Merlin 61 installation under C.R.D. contract, the additional two aircraft being intended for the U.S.A.

Back in Inglewood, California things were not, apparently, running as smoothly as they were at Hucknall. Philip Legarra, North American's Field Service Representative in the UK, and no doubt Tommy Hitchcock, were becoming concerned with the lack of progress with the American conversion. The licensed production of the Merlin 61 was not yet under way at Packard's though an English example had been shipped to the USA in August.

Legarra was pushing hard for the Packard Merlin 28 to be installed and although this engine, operating at +16 lb boost, would endow the Mustang with a performance inferior to the Merlin 61 it would, nevertheless, produce a fighter with a genuine 400 mph capability. However, it was not to be. By the late summer of 1942, much to many people's regret, all interest in this version was dropped and the decision taken to concentrate only on the two-stage Merlin 61 variant. Even so, nobody appeared to be in any hurry to get things moving.

Lp.8/JL.   5th August, 1942.

Major Hitchcock,
American Embassy,
London.

Dear Major Hitchcock,

With reference to our telephone conversation yesterday we confirm that we shall be delighted to see both you and Dr. Warner[23] on Friday next - 7th August - at Hucknall and Derby.

It is understood that you are flying to Hucknall, weather permitting, and I suggest that if you arrive between 11.30 and 12. noon you proceed straight to Derby for lunch, look around the Works and then return to Hucknall to spend some time with Mr. Dorey before leaving again for London.

I regret to say that Mr. Hives will be absent in Glasgow, but an early opportunity will be taken of arranging a meeting between he and Dr. Warner in London.

---

[23] Dr Edward P Warner Hon.FRAeS, Vice Chairman of the Civil Aeronautics Board who was in England during August and September 1942. His business with Rolls-Royce has not been ascertained but there can be little doubt that it had something to do with the Mustang. From 1920 to 1926 he was Professor of Aeronautical Engineering at Massachusetts Institute of Technology. He was the designer of the first wind tunnel at Langley Field, home of the Engineering Division of the Army Air Service and NACA, the National Advisory Committee for Aeronautics, in 1919.

FORM NO. 8a.

WESTERN UNION
(THE WESTERN UNION TELEGRAPH COMPANY)
CABLEGRAM

ANGLO-AMERICAN TELEGRAPH CO. LD.   CANADIAN NATIONAL TEL...
RECEIVED AT THAMES HOUSE, MILLBANK, LONDON, S.W.1. (Tel. No. Victoria 2541)   2941

TH4 INGLEWOOD CALIF 87/86 1/46/45 7 807... 27

LC LAPPIN
NORTHAMERICAN AVIATION INC
STJOHNSHOUSE SMITHSQUARE LONDON=

:NC17486 SORRY NO REPLY SOONER. INFORMATION DIFFICULT TO
OBTAIN AND TRANSMIT. BUMP WE QUESTIONED NOT DESIRABLE BUT
NOT DANGEROUS. YOUR PRESENT PLAN SHOULD BE FOLLOWED.
SUMMARY OF COMMENTS FOLLOWS WITH ME. PROGRESS ON PLAN
HERE PARALLEL TO YOURS IS QUITE GOOD. MORE COMPLETE
REARRANGEMENT BEING DONE. DATA FOLLOWS WITH ME. 28 IS
GIVEN IMMEDIATE CONSIDERATION AND LOOKS VERY PROMISING.
TENTATIVE FIGURES ON NEWEST PROJECT AVAILABLE
APPROXIMATELY AUGUST 16. EXPECT MY RETURN AUGUST 23=

NORTHAMERICAN AVIATION INC
PHILIP LEGARRA.

Please send your Reply "Via WESTERN UNION" You may telephone us for a messenger

CABLE AND WIRELESS
LIMITED

"*Via Imperial*"

Circuit.	Clerk's Marks.	Time Received.	
WEMUEHT18 F/W		921i	T 72

GBK496 INGLEWOOD CALIF 46/45 22 1748

LC MR LAPPIN CARE NORTH AMERICAN AVIATION INC
STJOHNS HOUSE SMITHSQUARE LONDON =
NC18410 PROGRESS NORMAL HERE. WE HAVE WORK TO DO ON
MY RETURN. HOPE TO RETURN EARLY SEPTEMBER. ENGLISH
INSTALLATION MOST IMPORTANT. TWO GOOD TECHNICAL MEN
ACCOMPANYING ME = NORTH AMERICAN AVIATION INC
PHILIP LEGARRA +

496 NC18410 +   GE/W

(L & P R)   NO ENQUIRY RESPECTING THIS TELEGRAM CAN BE ATTENDED TO WITHOUT PRODUCTION OF THIS COPY. REPLIES SHOULD BE HANDED IN AT ONE OF THE COMPANY'S OFFICES.

Lp.4/JL.   27th August, 1942.

Major Hitchcock,
American Embassy,
London.

Dear Major,

We have had some of your distinguished Army Air Corp here, including General Echols.[24] They have had a good look around Hucknall, spent the night and finished off looking through the Experimental Department this morning, and I hope they were satisfied with their visit. They were accompanied by Air Marshall Linnell and Air Marshall Hill.[25]

How are you ? Have you any recent news about the 'Mustang'. I still feel a little regretful that they did not put in, as originally, through you, a Packard Merlin 28 engine.

ARMY AIR FORCES
HEADQUARTERS, MATERIEL COMMAND
INTER-DESK MEMORANDUM

To: Colonel Chidlaw[26]   AFAMC-5

SUBJECT: Data left by Mr. Burton Date: August 28, 1942

Left by Alec Burton[27] together with the dope on the Griffon 61, this date. "Dutch" Kindleberger[28] says the Merlin 28 is out for installation in the P-51, but they are going full blast on the Merlin 61. About all the re-design necessary is to move the wing forward 3 inches and down 1 inch; also, the nose will be dropped a little to give better visibility than the P-51.

If the aerodynamics isn't ruined, looks like they might have a pretty good airplane.

From: J.F. PHILLIPS, COL., A.C.
W-7135,A.F.

LP.4/JL.   8th September, 1942.

Wing Commander I.R. Campbell-Orde,
Air Fighting Development Unit,
Royal Air Force,
Duxford,
Cambs.

My dear Orde,

Is it possible to see a copy of your report on your trials against the F.W.190, and if you have a similar report about the 'Lightning' I should very much like to see it.

Legarra has come back from America, and we are really beginning to turn the heat on in regard to this 'Mustang' project, as I feel it is going

---

[24] Major General Oliver P Echols, Assistant Chief of Air Staff, Materiel, Maintenance and Distribution Division, Washington. He had been responsible for getting production of the Merlin underway at Packard.

[25] Controller of Technical Services, British Air Commission in Washington.

[26] Colonel (later General) Benjamin W Chidlaw was head of Experimental Engineering at Materiel Command.

[27] Alexander T Burton, North American Aviation's technical representative for the Harvard in Britain. (Philip Legarra was their technical representative for the Mustang).

[28] James H Kindelberger, President of North American Aviation.

to be a very valuable fighter, when you bear in mind that the machine in which the Americans have gone nap - the 'Thunderbolt' - weighs over 13,000 lb.

Lp.11/JMB.   8th September 1942.

J. Ellor, Esq.,
The Packard Motor Car Co. Ltd.,
Detroit,
Michigan.
U.S.A.

My dear Jimmy,

I brought Mr. Legarra to Hucknall yesterday to discuss the futher developments of the Mustang, and the situation in the U.S.A. does not seem to be a happy one. Here we have an aircraft, which from the point of view of aircraft, is outstanding, and even with a Packard 28, it would have a performance probably round about 400 m.p.h. However, I suppose it is one of those situations, where in America you do not know where to start in order to get a large number of people with divergent views to see the common sense policy. However, we are taking energetic action as far as possible in order to impress upon the Air Ministry here and the American Air Corps, that this machine should enjoy a very high priority, which at the moment, it has not got.

Meanwhile at Hucknall, the conversion of the first aircraft was well underway. The number of aircraft allocated for modification had risen to five by the arrival in August of two more aircraft, AM203 and AM208. Two of the five were earmarked for evaluation by the US Army Air Corps. It was intended to convert a sixth aircraft thus giving the Americans three to experiment with but the proposal was not following through.

The installation

The substitution of a Merlin for the Allison did not pose any real headaches though some details needed close attention. Whilst the Merlin was perfectly capable of inhabiting the confines of the cowling without resorting to bulges and blisters there remained the problem of suspending it. The width across the Merlin's supercharger casing was greater than the distance between the existing engine mounting pick-up points on the firewall. This was overcome by the construction of an intermediate mounting that came away from the bulkhead in a shallow V fashion until the outermost points straddled the blower casing. From these points was hung the Rolls-Royce Consus (convergent suspension) mounting incorporating rubber-sprung pick-ups onto which the engine was bolted.

The next obstacle lay in the positioning of the air-intake feeding the carburettor. The original Allison engine had a downdraught arrangement whereas the Merlin's was updraught. The air for the Allison was received from a small intake on top of the cowling, just behind spinner. Obviously, this would not do for the Merlin whose requirement was for air to be supplied from somewhere beneath the engine. It was proposed to utilise this intake as an

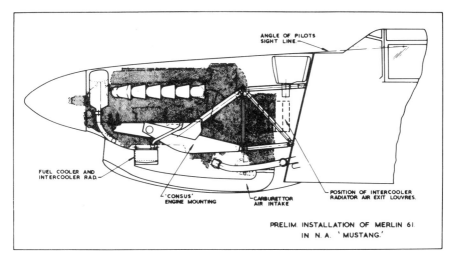

ANGLE OF PILOTS
SIGHT LINE.

FUEL COOLER AND
INTERCOOLER RAD.

'CONSUS'
ENGINE MOUNTING

CARBURETTOR
AIR INTAKE

POSITION OF INTERCOOLER
RADIATOR AIR EXIT LOUVRES.

PRELIM. INSTALLATION OF MERLIN 61.
IN N. A. 'MUSTANG.'

The original installation drawing of the Merlin 61 scheme showing the bifurcating of the airflow into the intercooler/ fuel cooler radiator and the carburettor air intake. The mounting from the original bulkhead pick-ups which straddled the supercharger before giving location the Consus engine mounting is also clearly seen. As seen here the engine features an SU type carburettor which protruded lower than the Bendix-Stromberg instrument that was actually fitted. After a few flights the lower line of the cowling was relieved of its bulge to make it continuous with the fuselage profile.

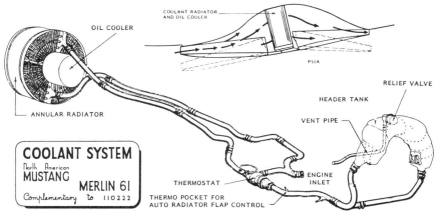

OIL COOLER

COOLANT RADIATOR
AND OIL COOLER

PSIA

ANNULAR RADIATOR

RELIEF VALVE

HEADER TANK

VENT PIPE

COOLANT SYSTEM
North American
MUSTANG
MERLIN 61
Complementary to 110222

THERMOSTAT

THERMO POCKET FOR
AUTO RADIATOR FLAP CONTROL

ENGINE
INLET

The original scheme drawing for the Mustang X cooling system. All pipework through the fuselage was original but the radiator and oil cooler units were manufactured by Morris Radiators. The radiator itself was of the curved fin and tube (secondary surface) type, identical in size to the original American unit which employed a honeycomb construction. It had to cope with a 33% increase in heat dissipation and did so admirably but wind tunnel tests revealed that a rectangular shaped matrice of the same area would perform even better. Inset is a cross section through the original radiator duct and shows the extent to which the troublesome front air scoop was capable of opening. At 3000 rpm the Merlin was pumping coolant at the rate of 120 gallons per minute. This diagram can be compared with that of the P-51B shown on page 76.

31

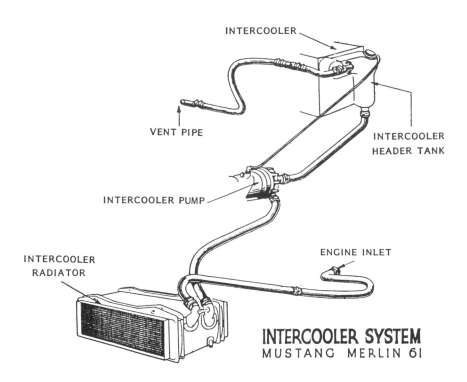

INTERCOOLER

VENT PIPE

INTERCOOLER
HEADER TANK

INTERCOOLER PUMP

ENGINE INLET

INTERCOOLER
RADIATOR

INTERCOOLER SYSTEM
MUSTANG MERLIN 61

The intercooler system which was entirely separate from the main coolant circuit. The header tank is shown here as integral with the intercooler itself though this feature was not embodied until the advent of the Merlin 66, prior to which a separate tank was mounted on the bulkhead. Not shown is the fuel cooler matrix which shared space in the intercooler radiator block on the prototype aircraft, even though it was never used after the early flights. The oil cooler, shown on next page, was of the honeycomb type and differed from the original American unit in that it projected proud of the main radiator instead of being buried within it.

airscoop for the intercooler radiator which would simplify matters by retaining most of the existing cowling and its structure and in doing so would permit close positioning of the matrix with the intercooler itself. Design along these lines was in hand when criticism was levelled at the sight line over the top of the cowling. This, it was claimed, did not give sufficient sighting of the target when it was positioned at the bottom of the deflection ring. The point was accepted with the result that the air-intake was deleted from the top of the cowling and the intercooler[29] radiator positioned beneath the engine. As there now had to be a large airscoop within the structure of the cowling it was decided that it would be practical to utilise this intake as an air feed to the carburettor, thus solving both problems. Visually the nose of the aircraft now

[29] See Appendix VI.

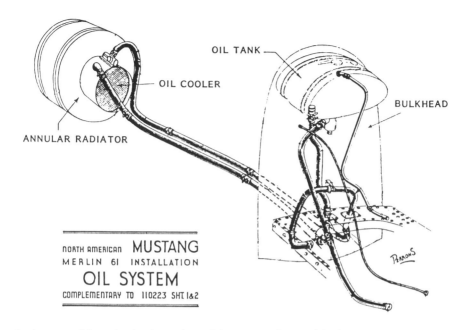

OIL TANK

OIL COOLER

BULKHEAD

ANNULAR RADIATOR

NORTH AMERICAN MUSTANG
MERLIN 61 INSTALLATION
OIL SYSTEM
COMPLEMENTARY TO 110223 SHT 1&2

had a very blunt look about it and in comparison with the sleek lines of the Allison installation did nothing to enhance the aircraft's undeniable beauty. However, the result was that the sight line was improved by 1 1/2 degrees. The ideal place for the intercooler radiator was, of course, within the main radiator duct, but as an enlarged version of the original American radiator matrix was to be employed, with its integral oil cooler, this was out of the question.

From this preliminary layout it was noticed that the spinner was 3 1/2 inches below the sight line and so, in an effort to reduce the bulkiness of the lower cowling, the thrust line of the engine was raised by this amount. In other words the engine itself was elevated by 3 1/2 inches. This resulted in the top cowling line lying for most of its length along the sight line whilst the 1 1/2 degrees improvement was maintained.

With the engine now sitting higher on the bulkhead it was possible to provide a reasonable air-intake elbow to the updraught carburettor and to keep the trunking that fed it within the confines of the bulkhead bottom line. This was considered to be an important design feature as the undercarriage door arrangement would not permit an external airscoop protruding through the skin at this point (a la Hurricane) should the utilisation of the intercooler radiator air-intake proved awkward. The position of the main coolant radiator and oil cooler was unaltered and remained within the ventral fairing beneath the rear fuselage. New units were manufactured by Morris, the radiator being slightly larger in area, the oil cooler slightly smaller.

The existing fuel system was not satisfactory for operation up to the proposed altitude of 41,000 ft. Initially it was proposed that a pressurised system be installed in place of the existing electrically-driven booster pump, but by the time the conversion was under way the system of an immersed fuel pump in each tank had been decided upon. This system enabled the deletion of the fuel cooler[30] from its position along side of the intercooler radiator (though this was so, an unconnected fuel cooler was fitted for the initial conversion). Further to this, tests with a Spitfire IX had shown that fuel would not 'boil' if a Bendix-Stromberg fuel injector was used. The standard fuel tanks would have to be replaced, by two tinned-steel units, in order to accommodate the immersed pumps.

Two types of propellor were to be evaluated. They were a specially constructed four-blader with a diameter of 11 ft 4 in. and the standard Spitfire IX four-bladed unit of 10 ft 9 in. diameter. Both were manufactured by Rotol and made of the wood laminate Hydulignum. The only alteration to the hydraulic system was to permit its operation of the supercharger speed control and the automatic radiator flap (later changed to pneumatic).

By early October the conversion was complete, the final touch being applied on the 12th when the engine was installed for the last time and AL975, now with a -G suffix, was rolled out for ground running. The new Mustang was now known as the Mark 10, or X as it was written in those days. Chronologically it should have been Mark III, but just as Canadian-built Hurricanes and Lancasters were given the same type number, well clear of British production, the new Mustang was similarly enumerated.

Meanwhile, over in the USA North American had commenced work on its first conversion and over on the east coast the first Packard versions of the Merlin 61 were undergoing test. Trouble was being experienced with the engine resulting in at least two failures and the power output was much lower than the British counterpart. These setbacks were to result in a delayed first flight of the American prototype aircraft and a greater delay in the delivery of production engines, for which aircraft had been build. Back in Britain Sir Wilfrid Freeman envisaged a Packard Merlin in a British Mustang. Whether he had squadrons of such aircraft in mind or just the flight testing of the American product at Hucknall is not known.

HEADQUARTERS
EUROPEAN THEATER OF OPERATIONS
UNITED STATES ARMY

ATS 452   4th September, 1942.

E. W. Hives, Esq.,
General Manager,
Messrs. Rolls Royce Ltd.,
Derby.

Dear Mr. Hives,
    We had received a report from Colonel Chidlaw, Assistant Chief of Staff to General Echols, on progress with the installation of the Merlin 61 engine in the Mustang in America.

---

[30] A fuel cooler was considered essential with a pressurised system to prevent the fuel from "boiling" on leaving the tanks and entering the float chamber (the Bendix-Stromberg carburettor did not have a float chamber).

The Mustang, now known in America as the P-51, will be known as the XP78 when fitted with the Merlin 61, which is itself known as the Packard V-1650-3.

North American estimate that the first airplane will be ready for flight by October 1st, and the second two to four weeks later. This promise is contingent upon Packard keeping their engine delivery date of September 1st.

One engine was delivered by Packard to Wright Field some time ago for calibration; after this it was returned to Packard for installation of improved connecting rods and a larger carburettor, and should have been returned to Wright Field again for further calibration on August 29th. The engines which will be delivered to North American will have the improved connecting rods, but what power will be taken from this engine will be determined by endurance tests at Wright Field.

On the basis of Rolls Royce performance figures, North American estimate the following performance for the XP78 airplane:

Gross Weight -	8,350 lbs.	(2-20 mm. cannon only - pilot's armor plate and certain ratio equipment not included in gross weight.)
High speed -	Sea Level	340 m.p.h.
	16,500 ft.	420 m.p.h.
	28,000 ft.	445 m.p.h.
Rate of climb -	Sea Level	3,460 ft./min.
	13,000 ft.	3,530 ft./min.
	20,000 ft.	2,580 ft./min.
	25,000 ft.	2,400 ft./min.
Service Ceiling -	42,400 ft.	

The foregoing is based on the following maximum power ratings:

1,375 b.h.p. at Sea Level
1,520 b.h.p. at 13,000 ft. (no ram)
1,300 b.h.p. at 24,000 ft. (no ram)

It may well be possible to fly the airplane on or about October 1st at the following ratings, which have been checked out on Wright Field calibration stand:

1,035 b.h.p. at Sea level
1,225 b.h.p. at 17,700 ft.
1,025 b.h.p. at 28,000 ft.

Colonel Chidlaw reports that no action has been taken relative to the Griffon engine, as there is little doubt that the Mustang would have to be largely redesigned to instal this engine.

They ask, however, to be advised regarding the delivery date of two Griffon 61 engines and spare parts, and to be sent complete information on this engine, including sufficient data to study its possible installation, as soon as possible.

Sincerely yours,

A. J. LYON,
Brig.General, A.U.S.   Air Technical Section

MOST SECRET

(Dept.O.A.)

23rd September, 1942.

My dear Kim

Can you give me some information as
to when the Merlin 61 will be produced by the
Packard Company, and what difference there is
between your version of this engine and theirs.

I would also like to know whether the
Mustang, as altered by you to take the
Merlin 61, will also take the Packard version
thereof.

Yours sincerely,

W.R. Freeman -

Hs.10/KW   28th September, 1942.

Air Chief Marshal Sir Wilfred R. Freeman,
V.C.A.S.,
Air Ministry (Dept. O.A.),
King Charles Street,
Whitehall, S.W.1.

Dear Sir Wilfred,

Replying to your letter of the 23rd, the Packard Merlin 61 engine differs
from the Derby version by the fact that it has a different type of two-
speed gear. As long as it works and is reliable there is no objection to
this, except of course the usual difficulties as regards spares.

They have an engine running, and had it at Wright Field, and so far as
our information goes they appear to be satisfied with it.

The calibration of Wright Field showed less altitude performance than
we get on our type, but this was anticipated and pointed out to them
because they were trying to use the standard carburettor, whereas our
tests had shown it was essential to increase the size of the carburettor.

From the information we have, the worst point which affects interchage-
ability is the position of the air intake on the carburettor. The drawings
show this to be approximately 1 1/2" further forward. If this is retained
it means that the engines cannot be installationally inter-changeable. We
are, however, pressing that as they have got to make a change in the size
of the carburettor, they take advantage of this and try and line up the air
intake position so that it is interchangeable with ours. If this is done there
should be no serious difficulty in installation.

Our Mustang at Hucknall should be flying in about 14 days' time, fitted
with the Merlin 61.

Legarra has been on the telephone this morning, having recently had contact with a Colonel who has come over from Wright Field and has now returned to the U.S.A., who apparently spoke in very disparaging terms of the Merlin 61 on test at Wright Field, and mentioned that it had blown up twice at 12 lb. boost.

Not feeling very good this morning I nearly said 'Pearl Harbour' to Legarra. However, I point out to him there were a number of Squadrons operating very satisfactorily with this engine installed, and I thought the best thing he could do was to get an unbiased impression of the situation from Major Bulman or Air Vice Marshall Linnell and this he is doing.

P.S. Since dictating the above, I have made further enquiries and find that the criticisms refer to Packard Merlin 61, and the failures appear to have been connecting rods and clutch, all at 12 lb. boost. The danger would appear to be that the attitude of Wright Field would defer the programme for Mustang aircraft until they had completed what they consider satisfactory test, and you may think it advisable to send a cable to Ellor to patch the matter up at Wright Field.

This concludes the first part of the story which has related events leading up to the first flight of the Merlin powered Mustang. Five days before the event took place, Major Hitchcock wrote a memorandum giving a brief resume of the story so far and its reproduction here provides an appropriate recap.

8 October 1942

MEMORANDUM

SUBJECT: History of the Mustang P-51 Aircraft.

The Mustang P-51 was ordered by the English directly from the North American Company. The order did not pass through Wright Field, and the airplane probably does not conform fully with the Wright Field handbook.

In the Air Fighter Development Unit Report No.43, dated May 5, 1942, the Mustang is described as "an excellent low and medium altitude fighter and certainly the best American fighter that has so far reached this country". Comparisons were made with the Spitfire VB in which it was faster than the VB at all altitudes up to 25,000 feet. At 25,000 feet it went about the same speed as the Spitfire VB, although at this altitude the Allison engine was developing 290 less horsepower than the Merlin engine in the Spitfire. Estimates have been made that with the same horsepower Mustang is twenty to twenty five miles per hour faster than the Spitfire VB.

The reasons for the remarkably low drag of the Mustang are not fully understood on this side of the ocean. The English think it is only partly due to the laminar flow wing.

The Rolls people became very much interested in the possibilities of Mustang airframe with the Merlin engine. Estimates were made as to the speeds that could be obtained with the installation of the 61 and 20 Merlin. The Air Ministry instructed the Rolls people to install five Merlin 61 engines in Mustang airplanes. Simultaneously with this development it was arrange to have the North American Company install a Packard version of the Merlin 61 in the Mustang airframe. Requests were sent to the United States to have the Packard Company start manufacturing Merlin 61s as promptly as possible.

The interesting qualities of the Mustang airframe were brought to the attention of General Arnold and Admiral Towers when they were in London in June last, by the American Ambassador; Air Chief Marshal Sir Charles Portal, Chief of Air Staff; Air Chief Marshal Sir Sholto Douglas, Commander in Chief Fighter Command, and Air Marshal F.J.Linnell, Ministry of Aircraft Production - Research and Development. Robert Lovell, Assistant Secretary of War for Air, was also advised by letter dated June 5, 1942, of the importance which English and various American representatives attach to the Mustang airframe and the desirability of energetically pushing the Merlin development.

In Air Fighter Development Unit Report No.55 dated August 9, 1942, on the Tactical Trials of the Focke Wulf 190, in which comparisons were made of the fighting qualities of various English and American fighter planes with the FW.190, in all respects except rate of climb the Mustang appeared to do the best against the 190.

Dr. Edward Warner, when he was in this country in August and September, 1942, made considerable inquiry at Farborough as to the reason for the low drag of the Mustang airframe. The Farnborough technicians were only willing to ascribe a small amount of the added speed to the laminar flow wing. Dr. Warner's reports on this subject are of interest.

Mr. Legarra, North American representative, reported when he came back from the United States in the early part of September, that the Mustang had the lowest priority that could be granted to an airplane.

Air Chief Marshal Sir Wilfred Freeman, Vice-Chief of the Air Staff, on a suggestion made by Mr. Legarra of the North American Company that the Mustang could be assembled in England from parts fabricated in the United States, has wired to the United States to have a study made as to the feasibility of this plan.

COMMENT

The Mustang is one of the best, if not the best, fighter airframe that has been developed in the war up to date. It has no compressibility or flutter troubles, it is maneouvarable at high speeds, has the most rapid rate of roll of any plane except the Focke-Wulf 190, is easy to fly and has no nasty tricks. Its development and use in this theatre has suffered for various reasons. Sired by the English out of an American mother, the Mustang has had no parent in the Army Air Corps or at Wright Field to appreciate and push its good points. It arrived in England at a time when great emphasis was placed on high altitude performance, and because it was equipped with a low altitude engine, was of no particular interest to English Fighter Command. The Mustang was turned over to the English Army Co-operation Command, for low altitude work. It performed well at Dieppe. The pilots who fly the Mustang are most enthusiastic about its performance.

The development of the Mustang as a high altitude fighter will be brought about by cross-breeding it with the Merlin 61 engine. While the prospect of an English engine in an American airframe may appeal to the sentimental qualities of those individuals who are interested in furthering Anglo-American relationships by joining hands across the water, it does not fully satisfy important people on both sides of the Atlantic who seem more interested in pointing with pride to the development of a 100% national product than they are concerned with the very difficult problem of rapidly developing a fighter plane that will be superior to anything the Germans have.

THOMAS HITCHCOCK
Major, Air Corps
Asst. Military Air Attache

Three views of the Merlin 65 installation in AL975. Of particular interest is the Consus (Convergent Suspension) engine mounting so called because lines taken through the centres of the angled pickups would theoretically converge with their opposite counterpart. All the principal loads were carried by rubber in compression and it was this feature that made the engine of the Mustang X so noticeably smooth. The intercooler/fuel cooler radiator is seen below the engine.

AL975-G

With an all-up-weight of 9065 lb., AL975-G made a thirty minute flight on 13 October 1942 in the hands of the Company's Chief Test Pilot, Capt. R.T. Shepherd. The engine was Merlin 65 No.721 (RM.10.SM)[31] driving a 10 ft. 9 in. diameter propellor through a reduction gear ratio of .477:1. With the availability of this mark of Merlin the performance estimates were amended to show a top speed in FS gear of 427 mph at 21,000 ft and 392 mph in MS gear at 9600 ft. Because the tinned-steel fuel tanks with immersed pumps were not yet ready the preliminary flights were undertaken with the existing system which restricted the aircraft's altitude to a maximum of 18,000 ft and necessitated the supercharger operating in MS gear only.

During the first flight a speed of 376 mph was attained, but there was a pressure build-up within the cowling causing it to become loose. There then followed a series of speed tests to ascertain if any improvement could be achieved by redesign of the cowling ventilation arrangements and the main radiator ducting. The latter was original with regard to the inlet and exit areas whereas the air from the intercooler radiator flowed through the engine bay and out via louvres on both sides of the rear engine cowling. The performance

---

[31] Contrary to all that has been written before, the Merlin 61 never did fly in the Mustang X.

with this configuration was disappointing being some 16 mph below the predicted figure.

The initial modifications were exclusive to the main radiator duct. Its exit area was reduced from 1.80 sq ft to 0.70 sq ft in the closed position and from 2.70 sq ft to 1.70 sq ft in the open. Tests had revealed that sufficient cooling was available at these settings even in tropical conditions (see section covering trials with AM121). This improved the speed by 14 mph to within 2 mph of the target.

The second series of mods incorporated the substitution of a .42:1 reduction gear ratio in place of the .477:1 and the streamlining of the cowling ventilation louvres. This had the effect of reducing the speed by 2 mph to 388 mph. A larger intercooler radiator was then fitted, the extra area being obtained by the deletion of the fuel cooler.[32] The lower section of the cowling housing the carburettor air-intake was flattened to provide a continuous line with the underside of the fuselage. The result was the return of the previously lost 2 mph in speed plus a 9% improvement in intercooling.[33]. The intake mod had the effect of reducing the Full Throttle Height (FTH)[34] by 400 feet but despite this was considered worthwhile and so was incorporated in all the conversions.

Further mods for the seventh flight on 21 October involved the fitting of the 11 ft 4 in. diameter propellor plus the complete blanking off of the starboard cowling vent. No improvement was measured. The next flight, with all louvres, open actually produced a drop of 2 mph. The see-sawing of the performance figures no doubt caused some head scratching but the next series of tests would, it was hoped, dispel any doubts.

Commencing with the ninth flight the port wing contained one of the new tinned-steel fuel tanks with an immersed fuel pump. It was now possible to obtain a set of performance figures in both supercharger gears. At this stage it was thought that one reason for the speed being below prediction was air passing through the engine bay being ejected through the cowling joints at right-angles to the line of flight. To combat this ducting was installed to channel the air overboard directly from the rear of the intercooler radiator. The louvres were then blanked off. On 8 November a performance evaluation flight was made in which full use was made of both supercharger gears. The speed in MS equalled the previous highest of 2 mph short of the target, whilst in FS 413 mph was attained, 14mph below prediction. More frustration. However, the flight on the 13th must have cheered the team up when, with the Spitfire propellor refitted the speed in FS gear jumped to 422 mph. This was most perplexing as a higher engine power would be required to replace the blade area differential between the two airscrews. Flying in a coarser pitch would not be an answer as this would reduce the efficiency of the engine. All this was to prove that the performance figures with the Spitfire airscrew were contrary to expectation, being low below 26,000 ft and high above this altitude. (This

---

[32] The original intercooler radiator had a frontal area of .68 sq ft, later increased to .88 sq ft. The fuel cooler had a frontal area of .107 sq ft.
[33] See Appendix VI.
[34] See Appendix VI.

AL975-G, the first conversion. These three photographs, taken at roll-out, show well the bulged lower engine cowling briefly fitted to this aircraft. Note the proud cowling exit louvres, later modified to be flush with the skin. The variable intake scoop is shown slightly open and the exit flap fully open. It was by fixing and sealing the former that the design speed was eventually achieved. The troublesome undercarriage doors are seen fully open. Other points to note are the 10' 9" diameter Spitfire airscrew and the newly applied roundel and fin flash to conform to the revised national markings then coming into use. At this stage the aircraft still wore its original green/brown camouflage but on 19 November 1942 it was resprayed in Spitfire colours.

characteristic was later confirmed by Boscombe Down during tests with one of their aircraft.)

To D.T.D   17 October 1942.
The speed realisation is most encouraging. Soon we shall have a scream for Mustangs instead of Spitfire IX's !
C.R.D

With the project now beginning to show signs of measuring up to expectations all those that had worked on the conversions (as of November 1942) were treated to a commemorative dinner. Legend has it that a wager was laid between Rolls-Royce and the Americans as to who would be the first in the air. The book 'The Magic of a Name' says that the bet was between Hives and Colonel Llewellyn, the Minister of Aircraft Production. The latter would seem to be the more feasible answer for a number of reasons. At the time this was just another conversion and it is doubtful if its true significance had been appreciated. The fact that no British or American 'dignitaries' attended the dinner seems to bear this out as does the thought of such unprecedented benevolence by the Company in recognition of what was in those days a common occurrence. By all accounts it was not a night to remember. The dinner was almost cold and one of those invited never got anything because on his way to the canteen in the blackout he stumbled down a hole dug for the foundations of a new hangar and broke his arm!

During these early flights considerable trouble was experienced with the undercarriage doors opening in flight. This would occur in a dive when the aircraft developed a yawing motion at speeds nearing 460 ASI. It was discovered that the undercarriage wheel doors became unlocked and locked repeatedly, presumably with the change of attitude and the effect of wind forces due to yawing. Investigation revealed that the latches were maladjusted and following correction there was considerable improvement though the trouble did recur occasionally, necessitating the fitment of a warning device.

In actual fact the problem was more serious than first imagined. When the P-51B entered service there were a number of accidents involving the break-up of aircraft in the air and for which no explanation could be found. Eventually it was traced to the undercarriage doors becoming unlatched and the problem was quickly remedied. It is interesting to note, therefore, that the problem had manifested itself at least twelve months prior to the spate of incidents experienced in service and that initial modifications had not proved successful.

To evaluate the climbing performance with the Merlin 65, a series of timed climbs were undertaken in which the results could be compared with estimates based upon the Spitfire IX which, it had been assumed, would be somewhere near correct. Before these tests were attempted the cowling louvres were restored to their former use when it was found that the ducting idea was in no way responsible for the performance improvement. The results were as follows with estimates in brackets:-

Altitude	Rate of Climb (fpm)
Ground level	3880 (3440)
5,000 feet	3880 (3480)
10,000 feet	3500 (3100)
20,000 feet	2820 (2720)
30,000 feet	1300 (1300)

It can be seen that the rate of climb from ground level up to 10,000 feet was considerably better than the estimate, an improvement of 440 - 400 feet per minute being shown. Above this height the improvement was not maintained, from 13,000 feet up to 34,000 feet the figures being practically as estimated.

Before a series of partial climbs could be completed to determine the correct rate of climb, the engine suffered a bearing failure and was removed. The test was transferred to the second conversion, AM208, which was by now at Boscombe Down.

The replacement engine was Merlin 65 No.82445 which was to remain installed for 16 hours 25 mins flying before it was removed and installed in AM208. No performance figures were issued for this aircraft/engine combination but it can be assumed that the design speed was achieved following the modifications to the radiator air scoop as outlined in the section covering AM208. The next engine was Merlin 70 (RM.11.SM) No.83335, installed in February 1943. This engine was related in most respects to the Merlin 65 with the exception of having the supercharger gear ratios of the Merlin 61 and the propellor reduction gear ratio of .477:1 instead of .42:1, virtues which dictated that is performance was best suited to high altitudes. Maximum power output was 50 bhp less that the Merlin 65. This engine was installed for general development and comparative performance purposes and not with the intention of improving the breed.

The first prototype standing outside Number 4 hangar looking all the better with the redesigned lower engine cowling. The cowling louvres have been recessed flush with the skin. The -G suffix to the serial denoted that the aircraft should be guarded when away from its base.

This view of AL975 shows the temporary modification to the cowling to allow the air from the intercooler radiator to be piped directly overboard instead of passing through the engine bay and out via the louvres. Blanking plates are shown fitted to the louvres. (Photograph Crown Copyright).

45

During the previous November, the second conversion, AM208, had flown and been despatched to the Aeroplane and Armament Experimental Establishment (A&AEE) at Boscombe Down for performance trials. During their evaluation various adverse comments were received of the directional stability and behaviour of the Mustang X and in consequence a series of tests were undertaken with AM208 to investigate the complaints. It appeared that there was a large change in directional trim with power and speed applied and the aircraft sideslipped easily during manouvres. This, it was thought, was due to a lack of fin area coupled with the effects from the four-bladed airscrew. However, the tests concluded that there was no real deficiency in the fin area but the fitment of a dorsal fillet to the base of the fin would improve matters to some extent.[35]

The dorsal fin mod, however, was only a partial success and in the April it was removed and the whole leading edge of the fin extended to increase the fin area by three square feet. This greatly improved the aircraft's stability, even when being flown hands-off, though aileron control at high speeds was poor.

Minutes of a Meeting held at Rolls-Royce, Hucknall, on February 2nd to discuss Directional Control on Mustang X aircraft.

The following were present:-

Mr. J. C. K. Shipp	D.A.N.A.2.
Wing Commander D. O. Finlay	O.C., A.F.D.U.
Squadron Leader E. S. Smith	A.F.D.U.
Mr. M. B. Morgan	Aero Department, R.A.E.
Captain R. T. Shepherd	Chief Test Pilot, Rolls Royce
Mr. W. A. Horrocks	Rolls Royce, Hucknall
Mr. W. Challier	Rolls Royce Performance
Mr. W. H. Sutcliffe	Rolls Royce Liaison
Mr. W. Collyer	Rolls Royce Flight Test
Mr. W. Jones	R.T.O., Rolls Royce
Mr. R.F. Beardslee	North American Aviation
Mr. E. Greenwood	Chief Test Pilot A.S.T.
Mr. E. E. Fairbrother	A.S.T.
Mr. J. Harvey	A.S.T.

Arising from AFDU's criticism of the directional control on the Mustang X a meeting was held at Rolls Royce, Hucknall on February 2nd, 1943. AFDU cannot accept the aircraft as a one hundred per cent success as a fighter machine at present and their criticisms are, in general, confirmed by Mr. Greenwood and Captain Shepherd.

It became apparent that there are two problems. The first is to provide sufficient directional stability and the second is to overcome the large change of directional trim with power which is objectionable owing to the heavy rudder forces involved.

Regarding the first problem AFDU state that during manoeuvres the aircraft side slipped very easily due presumably to increased gyroscopic effect combined with decreased directional stability due to the fin effect of the air-screw. The present 11ft.4in. air-screw has, of course, a much

---

[35] It was calculated that fitting the Merlin 65 to the Mustang resulted in a 44% loss in directional stability, equivalent to a fin area of 3.8 sq. ft. The original dorsal fin mod was a Rolls-Royce / NAA proposal and added another two square feet to the fin area. In the event the problem remained with the Mustang up until the appearance of the P-51H with its tall fin.

greater solidity when compared with the Allison installation (increased from 0.096 to 0.135). Mr. Morgan explained that the same difficulties are arising with other high powered aircraft. Messrs. Rolls Royce have, with the co-operation of North American Aviation, added an extra piece of fin area and Captain Shepherd considered this to be an improvement, but not the complete answer. Mr. Morgan was provided by Mr. Horrocks with sufficient information to estimate the effective loss in fin area. The Rolls Royce fin installation was examined and accepted by D.A.N.A.2. for their flights. Mr. Horrocks provided Mr. Fairbrother with details and drawings to enable AST to check stress the installation which is to be fitted on AL 963 for flight test by AFDU pilots. In the meantime, Messrs. Rolls Royce will carry out a further small fin modification on AL 975.

The second problem of the large change of directional trim with power, which has also been commented upon by A. & A.E.E., might be solved by the addition of either a booster tab or preferably by the addition of spring tab. The disadvantage of the booster tab is that the present rudder, while heavy for large angles, is light at small angles and may overbalance with the booster tab. The addition of a spring tab has every advantage and may solve the first problem at the same time as the second if there is a sufficient margin of directional stability left. Mr. Morgan is checking this point.

It was considered that a spring tab development should proceed for Mustang X aircraft and to avoid delay it was agreed that Mr. Fairbrother should visit R.A.E. with representatives of North American Aviation on Thursday, 4th February to discuss this development which will proceed at A.S.T. It might be considered desirable to send the fifth Mustang X AM 121 to A.S.T. for installation work. This aircraft will be complete in two days time and AD/D.A.N.A. is asked to give a decision.

To: Lp.   Dor/Hks.1/FEB. 5.2.43.

We have had a flying visit from Legarra and he brought with him photographs showing the N.A. conversion to 61 Mustang.

Legarra said that Schmued - Chief Designer at North American - is expected in this country in the course of about 10 days. I gathered that one of the things he particularly wanted to discuss was the re-actions over here to the question of aircraft handling with Merlin 61 installed.

There is still no news of the N.A.A. aircraft performance; we understood that they were having some trouble with what they term 'rumbling in the air duct'.

We have also had a discussion with Finlay and Smith from Duxford with regard to Mustang handling. Shepherd has flown our aircraft fitted with the additional Dorsal fin and says it is some improvement from the point of view of directional control in the power on and off condition.

We have one of the two Duxford aircraft back here now to fit the same Dorsal fin and this will be returned to Duxford in the course of a day or two for them to do trials themselves.

It seems to be generally agreed now between all the pilots that the directional stability in a dive is O.K. provided that the undercarriage wheel flaps remain closed as they now do with the additional hooks that we fitted.

The position of the five prototypes is as follows:-

The first one is at Hucknall for engine development with 14 S.M., 11 S.M. and 24.

The second one is at Hucknall awaiting an engine and will then be sent to Boscombe.

The third aircraft (the polished one) is at Duxford.

The fourth aircraft has been returned from Duxford for the fitting of Dorsal fin and will then go back to Duxford.

The fifth aircraft is at Hucknall and will be completed in a day or two and will then be sent to Duxford for the Americans.

Now that we have almost completed these five conversions, it becomes more than ever necessary to have another batch of aircraft for conversion, in order to avoid breaking down that section of the works that is on this job, and we are pressing M.A.P. on this matter.

At Hs.' request we are looking into the installation of Griffon 61 in standard Mustang.

Chr. is satisfied on the aerodynamic side but it will have to carry 230 lb. of ballast even without the C.R. airscrew and it will not be up to operational stress requirements. This, however, could be discussed with Schmued who might indicate how the aircraft could be reinforced sufficiently to meet Service operational requirements.

Mr. Horrocks.
Hucknall.   Lp.4/LA 8.2.43.

Thank you very much for your informative memorandum in regard to the Mustang, and I am glad to be brought up to date about the job.

It is a pity that any question of stability has now arisen, but I suppose under the circumstances it was unavoidable, and I hope we shall be able to satisfy the critics.

I am very interested to learn that the Chief Designer at North American is coming over, and I would like to be informed immediately he arrives in this country, as we want to have good talk with him on general policy, as for your private information I sometimes have a feeling that Legarra does not carry enough weight. They have done quite a bit of flying on the Mustang over there, and I have already been told about the rumbling in the air duct, and also had a promise that immediately they have any figures they will be cabled to the American authorities here and I shall get them right away.

With regard to future development of the Mustang, I feel the most important test to get clear is the one in which we can make a direct straightforward 'non-slide rule' comparison between the existing aeroplane and an aeroplane with the 24 for instance, so that we can clear up this doubt about the possible drag of the bump on the nose.

I am sorry about Dorey being stuck at home, probably by now feeling quite fit, and I expect he will end up by ignoring all doctor's instructions, returning to Hucknall, and giving you all scarlet fever.

The reference to the Merlin 24 installation came about from criticism of the air intake beneath the spinner, the 'bump on the nose' of the Merlin 65 Mustang, raised by eminent American aircraft representatives towards the end of 1942. Dorey suggested that a Merlin XX with Bendix carburettor (probably a Merlin 28) be fitted along with the deletion of the intercooler and its air intake. Such modifications along with a revision to the standard shape of the American installation would enable a performance calibration to prove or disprove the American contention. This particular suggestion was not proceeded with and instead the first flights of AL975 with the Merlin 70 were undertaken with the intercooler removed and the cowling modified to suit. Unfortunately, no details of the results obtained appear in the development report and although the test was repeated later with AL963, no satisfactory conclusions were achieved.

To: Lp.   Dor/Hks.1/FEB. 11.2.43.

We are doing the test, without the bump on the nose, next on the programme. We have not yet got the 24 but what we are doing is to fit the 11.S.M. which, is expected to-day, without an intercooler radiator, and get performance figures in M.S. with the bump removed, we shall then get the performance again with the intercooler radiator fitted, this should give us the story before Schmued arrives.

The position of the first five prototypes is now as follows:-

The 1st. one is at Hucknall for engine development (11.S.M. promised from Derby to-day).

The 2nd. is at Hucknall fitted with engine from 1st. aircraft and is ready to go to Boscombe.

The 3rd. aircraft (the polished one) is at Duxford.

The 4th. aircraft is at Hucknall; the Dorsal fin has now been fitted and it is now ready to go to Duxford.

The 5th. aircraft is now completed and is waiting to go to Duxford.

With the object of settling the stability question as quickly as possible, we are going over to Duxford a day or two after the 4th aircraft has been sent there in order to discuss their reactions to the Dorsal fin. I have had a talk with Legarra and he is going with us.

We want to make it clear to them, first, that we are doing something about it, and second, that the job can be put right. Legarra says that he has a rudder tab modification to follow up the Dorsal fin and it is expected that the two changes combined should make the job satisfactory.

It is understood that the rudder tab modification can be done in half a day or so.

SECRET

Hs.   Lp.6/LA 12.2.43.

During my visit to Legarra, I took some figures from his Production Chart in regard to Mustang, as follows:-

51.B 1943 Deliveries.		51.C. Deliveries.	
Feb.	2	April	6
March	65	May	26
April	188	June	125
May	145	July	189
		August	182
		Sept.	182
		Oct.	182
		Nov.	182
		Dec.	185

The Merlin 70 remained installed until May 1944 during which time a great deal of flying was engaged in the development of shunt cooling. This system,

Number 4 hangar at Hucknall where most of the aircraft conversions were undertaken right up to 1960's. In this picture, taken in April 1943, can be seen one of the Mustang X's, probably AL975, and Lancaster R5849 being converted to take Merlin 65 power-plants in the outboard positions.

The first prototype in its final form with a Merlin 70 installed parked in the "paddock" at Hucknall. Clearly discernable is the wide chord fin achieved by extending the leading edge by three inches. The cowling louvre has been angled, presumably to allow its air efflux to coincide with airflow pattern over the wing.

designed principally to prevent cavitation occurring under any coolant conditions at the pump impellor, offered considerable advantages over the standard arrangement, namely:

The performance of the system did not depend on the relief valve maintaining an air pressure in the header tank.

A standard engine could be used for underslung and wing installations.

The radiator design was not controlled by the liquid pressure drop characteristics and an appreciable reduction in the radiator operating pressure was obtained for wing installations. Furthermore, the dissipation could be increased due to increased tube velocities.

The design of the header tank was simplified and its position was more flexible. The increased performance in the circuit permitted a reduction in its capacity and the header tank could be made in light alloy due to not being subjected to main flow. On AL975 the header tank coolant capacity was reduced by 10 lb, and the tank itself weighed only 4 lb as against the normal 18 lb.

The wing system could be greatly simplified giving a further reduction in weight, a reduction in vulnerability and connections due to a reduction in plumbing.

The system could be arranged to give the full characteristics of the pump and by taking advantage of this the radiator suitability[36] would be increased by 5-8%.

The development of this system was granted priority as de Havilland was anxious to employ it on their DH 103 project, later to be named the Hornet.

Climbing speeds were also carried out with this installation and the following figures were recorded. It must be pointed out that when comparing them with those attained with the Merlin 65 installation the Merlin 70 was geared for high altitude work and so did not have the 'bottom end' performance.

Ground level	3290 fpm in MS	20,000 feet	2570 fpm in FS
5,000 feet	3310 fpm in MS	25,000 feet	2310 fpm in FS
10,000 feet	3330 fpm in MS	30,000 feet	1630 fpm in FS
15,000 feet	3040 fpm in MS	35,000 feet	950 fpm in FS

The absolute ceiling was 40,600 feet, service ceiling 40,100 feet and operational ceiling 37,800 feet.

Considerable trouble was experienced with the Merlin 70 installation due to engine oil breather losses resulting in an extremely dirty, oil-splashed aircraft. Along with other Mustang aircraft AL975 was employed (in parallel with the shunt cooling trials) upon the overcoming of this problem (see later chapter on oil system problems).

The final engine to be installed was Merlin 71 Special No.83025 fitted with an SU fuel injection pump. With this engine, which was merely a Merlin 70 with a cabin blower, AL975 was employed exclusively on the reliability of the shunt cooling system. Its career ended with an engine failure resulting in a wheels-up landing at Fradswell, near Uttoxeter. The aircraft was severely

---

[36] See Appendix VI.

AM208, the second conversion. This series of photographs were taken at A&AEE Boscombe Down in February and March 1943. The circled P marking denoting "prototype" was applied by the A&AEE and appeared only on this aircraft. The profile of the wing tip, in the side view, shows well the camber of the upper surface of the laminar flow wing whereby the highest point is at mid chord. Note also the hollow-ground effect of the wing's trailing edge. As far as can be ascertained AM208 was the only Mustang X photographed in the air (p.55). (Photos. Crown Copyright).

damaged and declared a write-off. Total time spent on Merlin development at Hucknall was 195 hours 30 mins.

AM208

This was the second conversion to be completed and made its first flight on 13 November 1942. Practically identical to AL975-G it differed only in having the main radiator front flap fixed permanently and sealed. This modification had been incorporated as tests with the Allison-powered AM121 thus treated had produced an increase in speed of 6 to 7 mph. With the exception of AL975-G all aircraft were so modified during conversion. AM208 and the three that followed never sported the bulged lower engine cowling, as had the prototype, which was designed to accommodate the Merlin 61's SU carburettor which, in the event, was never fitted to the Merlin 65.

Fitted with Merlin 65 No.81953 driving a 10 ft 9 in. diameter airscrew it was delivered to the A&AEE at Boscombe Down on 28 November after a preliminary two and a half hours of flying. There, during the following months, it was to undergo a series of performance tests, terminating in April, to determine the precise performance of the type which, with regard to AM208, was the aircraft modified to the latest standard. At 9100 lb it was slightly heavier than the prototype.

The preliminary tests were concerned with maximum speeds, the engine operating at the combat rating of + 18 lb. boost.

Maximum TAS at 2,000 feet	360 mph in MS
Maximum TAS at 10,800 feet	406 mph in MS (FTH)
Maximum TAS at 22,000 feet	433 mph in FS (FTH)

The change from MS gear to FS took place at 15,500 feet. The effect of the radiator intake modification was clearly responsible for an increase of 11 mph over AL975-G, thus taking the top speed well clear of the estimated 427 mph. Following these tests and prior to the climb trials it was noticed that the engine oil was in a poor condition. The aircraft was flown back to Hucknall for investigation but further problems arose and the decision was taken to change the engine. The new engine was No.82445, ex AL975 which, as mentioned earlier, had now inherited a Merlin 70. On 12 February 1943 AM208 left Hucknall for the last time and returned to Boscombe Down.

Although this engine did not perform so well as 81953, a promising set of climb figures were achieved. These revealed that the best climbing speed at combat rating was 195 mph up to 19,000 feet, decreasing by 7 mph per 2000 feet thereafter. The rate of climb in MS gear at the FTH of 7500 feet was 3560 fpm, whilst in FS gear at 19,000 feet it was 2840 fpm. The time-to-height figures were 2.9 min to 10,000 feet; 6.3 min to 20,000 feet and 11.3 min to 30,000 feet. The absolute ceiling was 39,000 feet. Full details of these tests can be found in Appendix III.

AM203

The third aircraft to be converted was sprayed in a high-speed glossy finish by Sanderson and Holmes, the Derby firm of coach builders. This was done

to determine the effect such a finish would have upon the performance of the Mustang in comparison with the standard matt scheme. AM203, like AM208, was not employed on any flying duties with the Allison installed but entered the shops for conversion immediately on arrival. It was fitted with Merlin 65 No.82509 driving the 11 ft 4 in. propeller and made its first flight on 13 December 1942 in the hands of Capt Shepherd.[37]

This aircraft was destined for the Air Fighting Development Unit at Duxford but prior to despatch was tested by Hucknall and the A&AEE, being flown to the latter on 16 December for a five day stay. Maximum speeds attained were 431 mph at 21,000 ft in FS gear and 403 mph at 10,400 ft in MS. The 10ft 9 in. propellor was then fitted and the tests repeated. Just as had happened with AL975-G there was an increase in speed, giving an addition 3 mph in FS. The larger propellor was then refitted and the aircraft flown to Duxford for a three-week stay prior to returning for modifications. During those three weeks a performance and tactical appraisal was made in comparison with the Spitfire IX with a Merlin 66 installed. The Merlin 66 was identical to the 65 except that the propellor reduction gear ratio was .477 as opposed to the latter's .42. Details of the trials are given in Appendix IV.

Following a further visit to Duxford it returned to Hucknall once again for a series of performance checks preceeding which the high speed finish was resprayed over in matt to compare the effect that the superior finish had upon the aircraft's performance. Whilst this work was in hand the enlarged-fin mod was incorporated. To everyone's surprise there was not the slightest variation in speed between the two finishes. It was then concluded that the superior

---

[37] All five prototypes, in fact, made their initial flights piloted by Ronnie Shepherd.

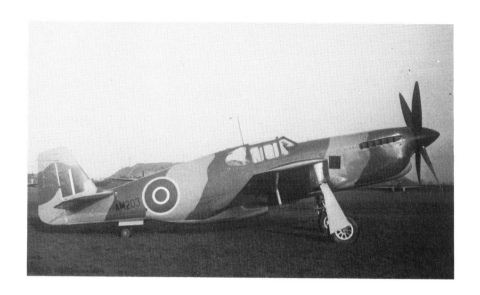

AM203, the third conversion. In order to evaluate the effect that a high-speed paint finish would have on performance it was sprayed accordingly by Sanderson and Holmes, the Derby firm of coachbuilders. It is seen here immediately following its conversion. No noticeable increase in speed was achieved and eventually the standard finish was applied.

AL963, the fourth conversion. This view shows clearly the dorsal fillet added to the base of the fin to give greater directional stability. As far as is known only AL975 was similarly modified before the change to a broader chord was implemented. (See also cover illustration).

design and construction of the Mustang, and in particular its external smoothness, could not be improved upon and that the design was aerodynamically clean (a point noted by the AFDU also).

With the completion of these tests AM203 was again despatched to the AFDU, which was by now at Wittering. Following a re-evaluation of its handling it returned to Hucknall where it was to remain unflown until declared redundant to requirements, after which it was despatched to 20 MU Aston Down.

The story of AM203 does not end there, however. Within a short while it was back at Hucknall, this time with 12 Group Communications Flight, on the RAF side of the airfield. Whilst there it was often flown by Sqn.Ldr. A G McIntyre who had been seconded to Rolls-Royce on behalf of the Fighter Pilot Engine Handling School. Athol McIntyre later joined Rolls-Royce where he remained until his retirement in 1981. Sadly, AM203 was prematurely retired in December 1944 for nothing more serious that a coolant leak in the engine. This had occurred whilst being flown by the No.2 to McIntyre's successor - a safe landing being made at Valley. Before any assessment could be made with regard to repair the Air Ministry had deemed such action not worthwhile and by the time that Rolls-Royce arrived at the scene it had been dismantled and removed.

AL963

This aircraft arrived at Hucknall on 26 June 1942 and like AL975 was employed for a short time on performance and handling trials prior to conversion. Merlin 65 No.82459 was then installed and following its acceptance flights it was despatched to the AFDU at Duxford for Service trials. A week later it was back at Hucknall for fitment of a dorsal fin after which it returned to Duxford for a couple of weeks before finally becoming resident at Hucknall for the remainder of its life.

Merlin 65 Special No.82551 was then installed operating at +23 lb boost and fed by a Mk.2 SU fuel injection pump. To prevent detonation when operating on 100 octane fuel the compression ratio was reduced from 6:1 to 5:1. The use of an SU pump in place of the Bendix-Stromberg was considered the most convenient method of producing the fuel metering characteristics necessitated by the increased fuel flow requirement. The ordinary float chamber and diaphragm types of carburettor were at this time approaching their limits when married to the two-stage Merlin and Griffon engines due to surging and inadequate metering conditions. The fuel injector pump was regarded as the final answer. The Bendix carburettor, which was diaphragm-controlled (floatless), sprayed the fuel into the eye of the first stage of the supercharger, as did the SU pump, but for it to meet the same requirements of the latter would have involved major modifications to the instrument itself.

The purpose of this installation was to obtain preliminary flight data for the RM.14.SM (Merlin 100) prior to its availability.[38] Flight tests totalled 7 hr 15 min after which the engine was derated back to +18 lb.

Maximum speed in mph

Altitude	1,000	5,000	10,000	15,000	21,000	25,000	30,000
Merlin 65 +18 lb	353	370	390	393	412	420	409
Merlin 65 +23 lb	370	387	394	409	424	420	409

From these results it can be seen that the higher boost rating gave an increase of 17 mph up to at least 5000 feet in MS gear and roughly the same amount from 15,000 to 19,000 feet in FS. The odd altitude of 21,000 feet is shown as this was the FTH at the higher rating.

Rate of Climb in fpm

Altitude	Ground level	3,000	5,000	10,000	15,000	20,000
Merlin 65 +18 lb	3000	3800	3800	3480	3040	2840
Merlin 65 +23 lb	4700	4700	4490	4000	3980	3160

This table shows that the rate of climb was improved by 900 fpm from ground level up to 3600 feet. This improvement gradually decreased up to the changeover from MS to FS (8400ft) where it had fallen to 200 fpm. With the change into high gear the increase commenced again, reaching its peak at 15,200 feet where it had risen to 940 fpm.

---

[38] The RM.14.SM incorporated an increased capacity supercharger giving higher Full Throttle Heights and operated at a maximum boost pressure of +25 lb.

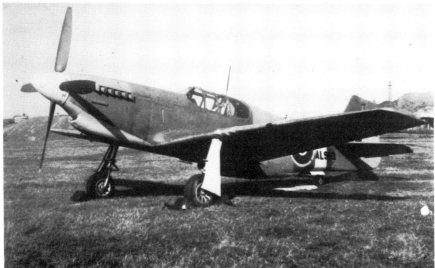

By resiting the intercooler radiator from the nose to the main radiator duct, where it was positioned behind the main coolant matrix, AL963 became the sleekest of the Mustang X family. Noticeable is the fin leading edge extension that had been grafted on in April 1943 to give a broader chord. Note also the blanking of the cowling louvres.

AM121, the fifth conversion. Although it was the first to arrive the conversion it was decided to retain the original configuration in order to investigate cooling drag problems. The clean lines of the Allison installation are apparent in this view as is the intake behind the spinner serving the downdraught carburettor. AM121 bears the old style roundel and fin flash which were superceded in the latter half of 1942 by those depicted in the other illustrations.

Flying with this engine totalled 45 hr 45 min, most of which was concerned with the endurance testing of the SU pump, after which it was replaced by Merlin 66 No.156369 for intercooler development. These tests were with an intercooler with an integral header tank containing the coolant whereas normally it was mounted separately on the bulkhead. At the same time the intercooler radiator was resited from its position under the nose and mounted in series with the main radiator in the central fairing. This enhanced the appearance of the aircraft by streamlining the nose which now had only a small intake sufficient only to feed the carburettor. The intercooler radiator occupied a position directly ahead of the main coolant matrix, a position which unfortunately compromised the efficiency of the latter. After 4 hr 20 min flying the aircraft was reverted back to the standard configuration, the highest speed attained being 422 mph at 22,400 feet.

This particular programme turned out to be a disappointment as an accurate performance calibration could not be obtained due to severe overheating problems caused by the masking of the main radiator, despite the fact that the exit area had been increased considerably. It is interesting to note that Hucknall still thought that the best place for the intercooler radiator was under the nose. Despite the many improvements that had been made at Inglewood to accommodate the Merlin, the fact was that the production aircraft were only 5 mph faster than the crude looking prototypes.

The final period of flying undertaken by AL963 was concerned with the reliability testing of the SU fuel injection pump, Merlin 65 Special No.82551, still rated as an RM.14.SM, being re-installed for a further 45 hours flying. The final flight took place on 6 January 1944 after which it was placed in storage prior to disposal.

AM121

As mentioned earlier this aircraft was the first to be sent to Hucknall for conversion; in the event it was the last to be completed. This aircraft was of the latest production standard being an NA-83 type (AG518 was an NA-73) and 730 lb. heavier than the first production models. An eight month period of performance and other work was undertaken before the conversion commenced, the most important of which was the investigations into the aerodynamics of the radiator duct.

The Mustang's heat transfer arrangements were very well thought out and in advance of contemporary British practice. When the latter had mounted its radiators in the central position the whole of the matrix was placed below the fuselage, usually beneath the centre section (a la Hurricane) or slightly ahead of it (Hart, Fury etc, though some of the Hawker designs were able to retract the radiator during the cruise regime). North American's approach was masterly in that more than half of the radiator/oil cooler was buried within the rear fuselage resulting in the least protrusion possible below the aircraft.[39] Where they went wrong was with the airscoop arrangement which was made variable to a much greater extent than was necessary thus compromising the good work achieved in drag reduction.

Initial flight tests with AM121 had shown that the excessive opening range of the radiator scoop caused an increase in drag too great to be tolerated on the RM.10.SM installation, even at climbing speed. Tests were undertaken to determine the drag characteristics of the duct in the standard operating condition and then with the scoop fixed to give smaller entry areas.[40] Reasons for the large entry area were not known but thought to be to reduce expansion loss or to meet ground cooling requirements. Airflow and drag characteristics were recorded with the scoop setting ranging from fully open (13 inches) to fully closed (4 inches). It was seen that a large proportion of the loss of flow caused by having the scoop fixed in the closed position was regained by opening it a small amount. As a result of these tests it was decided that for the first prototype conversion, AL975, the duct entry would be made variable over a range of only 4 to 6.5 inches. Top speed attained during these tests was 371 mph at 14,550 feet.

AM121 was converted to receive Merlin 65 No.721, the original engine installed in AL975-G. As no development flying was to be carried out with this

---

[39] This particular type of radiator installation was, in fact, previously employed by Curtiss on their XP-46 design, which did not go into production. However, the wind tunnel and flight performance results were purchased by North American in an effort to reduce the time taken to produce the Mustang prototype. This deal was undertaken by Lee Atwood, North American's Chief Engineer but, as he later revealed, the data was never referred to.

[40] Apparently, the sealing of the front scoop was recommended by Legarra and was initially implemented on an aircraft at Air Service Training at Hamble where an improvement of the order of 10 mph was recorded.

AM121 was eventually handed over to the USAAF 8th Fighter Command at Bovingdon and is seen here in full American markings, albeit still retaining its RAF serial. Points to note are the broad chord fin, the taped over gun ports which seem to indicate that this aircraft was used for gun firing or performance tests and the dark emission from the cowling louvres pointing to some kind of engine failure.

13·10·42	AL 975 G	0-30	SHEPHERD	—	12·30
13·11·42	AM 208.	0-30	SHEPHERD	-	15-10.
13·12·42	A.M 203.	1-00	SHEPHERD.	—	14·30
21.1.43	AL.963.	0-45	SHEPHERD.	—	14·35.
7.2.43.	AM 121	0.30	SHEPHERD.	—	16-00.

Extracts from the Hucknall flying log showing the entries depicting the first flights of each of the five prototypes Mustang X conversions. The right-hand column reveals the take-off time. They appear here in montage form for the sake of convenience.

aircraft it was despatched to the AFDU at Duxford for Service trials; they in turn loaned it to the 8th Fighter Command USAAF at Bovingdon. From here it returned to Hucknall to have the broad-chord fin fitted and eight days later it was loaned to Rotol at Staverton. During a fourteen day period it was to fly no less than 150 hours on evaluation of their Rotoloid propellor blade coating. This protective layer was only .020 inch in thickness and by the end of the test period was found to be unsuitable due to deterioration resulting in the shedding of large areas of the coating. A thicker application of .030 inch was recommended.

Back at Hucknall Merlin 65 No.82459 (ex AL963) was installed and after a final check over it was despatched for the last time to spend the rest of its life with the 8th Fighter Command's Air Technical Section at Bovingdon.

Meanwhile, back in California

In comparison with Inglewood, the problems encountered at Hucknall with their prototype conversions were insignificant. In the first three months from the XP-51B's first flight on 30 November up to the end of February, when a second aircraft had joined the programme, only 35 flights had been accomplished. By comparison Hucknall's first three months had seen three aircraft converted and 46 flights achieved and to this must be added the flights undertaken by Boscombe Down. When considering the climatic differences the Hucknall record speaks for itself. Although the comparison is slightly unfair in that North American were flying with a new engine, it must be said that the XP-51B's problems were basically of an aerodynamic nature and in particular with the radiator duct design.

The initial scheme featured a duct which was little more than a deepened version of the P-51A type and with which buffeting and overheating was experienced. Indeed, severe overheating was experienced on the first flight which was to ground the aircraft until late December. The problem was identified as silting up of the narrow water passages in the matrix, details of which are given elsewhere. A further problem was the uneven distribution of the airflow though the duct to the extent that the upper half of the radiator (mainly taken up by the intercooler matrix) was receiving insufficient air, the prime cause of which was the poor design of the duct intake. Furthermore, the radiator was installed on its side, to give convenient pipe runs down the duct side and also good access to the connections, which meant that the water passages ran east-west and the poor airflow through the duct deprived most of the upper tubes of cooling air. With the re-design of the duct the radiator was re-mounted in the vertical position.

Some of the problems experienced during the early months along with other points of interest were the subject of letters sent by Jimmy Ellor, Rolls-Royce's man at Packard in Detroit, the relevant details from which are reproduced here.

Lr/331/MG.   14.10.42

You have apparently beaten us to it on the flight of the 61 Mustang. Hope the performance is up to expectations.

At the request of U.S. aircraft constructors, the carburettor inlet flange face distance from the crankshaft centreline has been reduced to a

The first prototype American conversion, XP-51B 41-37352, which was flown for the first time on 30 November 1942, 6 weeks after Hucknall's first conversion. This aircraft, and the second prototype, were converted from two Mustang 1A airframes that were part of an RAF batch. Points to note are the deepened radiator duct with the original boundary layer gutter configuration, and the bulky profile of the air-intake trunking with its curve into the carburettor which protruded lower on the early Packard engines (this aircraft had engine number B.5 installed). The panel around the exhaust area, which featured neat extrusions around the individual stubs, has been left unpainted.

minimum in order to facilitate the arrangement of the air intake scoop without its projecting too far into the airstream.

The first flight engine is now installed in the aircraft and a flight is expected in about three weeks time but dated by radiator delivery. North American are still keen on installing a number of machines with the V-1650-1 but no decision has been reached on this project yet.

The first production model V-1650-3 is scheduled for December 15th. Packard will start delivery early next year working up to 225 engines per month in May. This depends upon the supply of machine tools promised by Washington under a high priority. It is thought that this figure will be stepped up considerably as the job progresses.

No major difficulties have been encountered but the piling up of endurance runs has been held up do to lack of V-1650-3 engines. Number One engine is about half way through its flight approval running under altitude conditions at Wright Field. These tests have been held up by plant failure and the damage to the super-charger when the sludge collected in the rotor shaft recess. The satisfactory completion of these tests is necessary before any machines will be permitted to fly. A second engine will be endurance running at Packard and the official Air Corps type test will follow the 50 hours flight development running at Wright Field.

I have recently visited the North American plant to discuss interchange-ability, production Mustang power plants, and to help their engineers on a few problems arising out of the flight trials on the two experimental Mustangs. Although some 30 flights have been made in the first airplane and about five on the second, the total time amounts to very little. Speed runs have been made at each critical altitude and furnished corrected speeds of 426 MPH at the high gear critical altitude of 28,600 feet and 405/410 on low gear at 16,000 feet.

These, however, are not regarded as representing the performance of the airplane since buffeting occurred in the regions of the radiator exit caused by a breakdown in air flow at the front of the duct. To obtain anywhere near stable conditions, the pilot had to fly level with his radiator flap open well beyond the normal position thus increasing the drag considerably.

In the early flights, serious trouble was experienced by hunting of the Hamilton four-bladed airscrew due to a faulty pilot valve in the control unit. The speed tests were made with the Aero Products four-blader (Blanchard-General Motors). Production aircraft will however be fitted with the Hamilton which weighs 440 lb.

In addition to the buffeting and airscrew troubles, the early flights disclosed cooling system trouble with high coolant drop through the radiator and rate of flows varying between 70 and 90 U.S. gallons/min.[41] North American have been sorting these out by extensive ground running. The total running time of No.1 airplane engine is about 70 hours and 30 hours on No.2, and more than half of this has been done on the ground. Fortunately the engines have given no trouble and are creating a very good impression. The pilots speak very highly of their smooth running and ease of operation.

PROSPECTS OF SUPPLYING BRITAIN WITH P-51B AIRFRAMES FOR INSTALLATION OF MERLIN 61 ENGINES

I raised this question with North American Aviation and was informed that their production schedule of complete airframes was based on the Packard V1650-3 engine delivery schedule. If, therefore, Packard meet their agreed schedule, Britain can only receive Mustangs with Packard V1650-3 engines and power plants. Airframes alone will only be available if Packard fall behind in deliveries - assuming that North American maintain their own schedule. The present estimate of engine production by Packard is that they will be one month behind in commencing deliveries but will be up to the promised production by the end of June. Ten aircraft are promised by the end of March after which production is schedule at 125 for April and 186 for May working up to a maximum of 400 per month about September. If Britain requires complete airframes to install Merlin 61 engines it will be necessary for B.A.C. to approach U.S.A.A.F. to increase production at North American.

Supply of complete airframes should not be confused with certain production parts which are to be sent over to assist in the manufacture of Mustang airframes in Britain.

A further point to be noted is a proposed change over from the P-51B to the P-51D after the first 400 aircraft. This change embodies moving the wing forward about three inches and improving the top engine cowl fairing

---

[41] Normal coolant flow rate at combat conditions (3000 rpm) was 145 US (120 Imperial) gallons per minute.

lines to effect better merging into the pilot's windscreen. This change will effect the top and bottom engine cowls and air-intake elbow and possibly on or two pipe runs to the radiators and oil cooler. The layout is not yet completed but no change is anticipated with regard to the general engine installation.

LIGHTENED MUSTANG

Design work is proceeding on a lightened version of Mustang and the North American chief designer, Mr Schmued, is now visiting Britain in connection with it. To effect weight saving lower factors on structures are being worked to. Weight is being designed out of the undercarriage using the smaller British type wheels, and lighter four-blader airscrews will be used, probably the wooden-bladed Rotol. The present Hamilton four-blader on the P-51B weighs 440 lb.

In order to save some weight, but most particularly to adjust balance, North American are proposing to delete the front header tank and place it above the radiator. This scheme is being tried out on a rig. In order to simplify the radiator ducts and eliminate oil system controls, North American intend to incorporate the liquid-cooled oil cooler system on this lightened airframe, if the preliminary tests now in hand prove successful. I have already described this system in a previous report and have received your comments. (For the sake of continuity Hucknall's comments are reproduced here - Author.)

Dor/EWS/Bt.1/MNH.   22.2.43.

N.A.Mustang.
XP-51F Cooling System using an Oil-Water Heat Exchanger.

We have examined the memo and data under the above heading dated December 17th. 1942 and would offer the following comments. These are further to our memo of the 2nd. November, 1942, which was forwarded per Mr. Ellor of Rolls-Royce Inc.Ltd., Michigan, in which we gave some preliminary comments on the principles of the system without having received the detailed information of the N.A. proposals.

(1) It is noted that the calculations are made for the condition of 3000 R.P.M. and 15 lb/sq.in. boost pressure, but somewhat increased heat input from the intercooler will result when the 18 lb. boost condition is reached. We also consider it advisable to provide for a higher percentage intercooling than the 35 - 40% mentioned in the memo. The sizes of the units are therefore somewhat optimistic for the conditions we have in view at present on our own installations.

(2) The weight analysis seems distinctly optimistic as we regard it inadvisable to delete the automatic oil control while the mounting weight quoted for the proposed heat exchanger seem extremely low.

The oil door which we assume to signify a flap for reducing the air flow over the oil cooler under coring conditions while admittedly eliminated, would not have been necessary in any case with a correctly designed oil cooler.

With the above points in view we do not consider that there will be any nett saving in weight with the new system, nor will there be any appreciable reduction in drag.

(3) The system does appear to eliminate the possibility of oil congealing in flight, but this can be achieved in any case by the correct design of the oil cooler. This does not present itself as a serious difficulty in our own installation.

(4) The inclusion of all cooling units in a single duct is possibly an advantage, but this can also be done in other ways, and recent tests render it doubtful whether the removal of the intercooler radiator from the nose position is likely to show any advantage.

(5) The principal objection to the scheme, as a whole is the increased vulnerability which results from the oil cooling being dependent on the charge cooling system. If any part of the latter is shot up the oil cooling is completely lost with fatal results to the aircraft; if the intercooler system is separate it is normally possible to continue flying in M.S. gear even after the coolant has been lost from the system.

To sum up, while we do not wish to discourage a try-out of this system we feel that it does not offer any very marked advantages over alternative schemes of proved reliability, particularly we regard the added vulnerability as a serious disadvantage.[42]

(Lr/347MG Cont)

The cooling system tests have shown:-

a. Insufficient air separator properties of the header tank due largely to their having departed from the recommended Spitfire scroll detail.
b. Difficult system to eliminate trapped air when filling.
c. Insufficient reserve water space in the header tank to make up for air space in the system.
d. Very high resistance of radiator and pipe lines which totalled 18 lb/sq.in. These are being remedied in the production system.
e. Uneven air flow at the face of the main and intercooler radiators. Modified arrangement for production.
f. Severe corrosion in the coolant systems after 10 hours due to ineffective protection of the preponderent aluminium. A measurable success has been achieved in their investigation of coatings.

By the time you receive this you will no doubt have met Mr. Schmued, North American chief designer who is now on a visit to Britain to obtain information on a proposed lightened Mustang. A similar project is proceeding in connection with the P-51A Allison engined machine. It is interesting to note that the war emergency rating now permitted on the Allison single-speed single-stage engine gives the Mustang a speed of 415 MPH at 11,000 feet altitude when the power is 1440 BHP.

INSTALLATION OF MERLIN 61 IN PRODUCTION MUSTANG AIRFRAME

From further drawing studies at North American and Packard, it would appear that the British Merlin 61 engine will fit into the production airframe provided the cabin blower drive is deleted from the side of the crankcase and if North American can arrange for increased clearance between the boost control linkage and the oil tank, also increased clearance locally between the intercooler pump outlet and the box section of the engine mounting. It is my understanding that the production Merlin 61 is fitted with the universal crankcase which has the cabin blower drive deleted making it similar at this point to the V1650-3 engine.

---

[42] If this advice was passed on to North American it went unheeded as all the lightweight Mustangs, the XP-51F/G/H series, utilised oil coolers deriving their coolant from the intercooler circuit.

It was agreed that the most effective way to ascertain what interchangeability really entailed would be to mount the Merlin 61 into a production Mustang airframe. This could either be done at the North American plant using the British Merlin now at Packard or to get Derby to do it by sending over to Britain the production parts involved. North American favour the latter procedure as Derby know more about the installation requirements of the Merlin 61. For this purpose Mr Rice, chief engineer at North American, suggests supplying Britain with a production engine mounting, the bulkhead with mounting attachments and oil tank fixed in place modified with a recess to give clearance to the boost control. A complete engine cowl will be included with air intakes. By the end of June parts should be in production for the P-51D and those which differ from the parts already supplied should be sent over to check the effect of these changes on their trial installation.

Hucknall should note that the wing on the production P-51B and P-51D is already three inches lower than the P-51A in which they are at present installing the Merlin 61's. With regard to the above suggestion of sending parts to Derby, it should be understood that North American will take no further action in this matter unless they are instructed by U.S.A.A.F.

Since the discussion took place at North American, arrangements have been made for Packard to despatch the British Merlin 61 to North American for them to make a trial installation in their production airframe. This was sent on Saturday, February 20, at the instruction of U.S.A.A.F. In my opinion it would be a great advantage for Britain also to make a trial installation and the suggestion of sending over existing parts quickly should receive consideration.

SPARK PLUGS

Production engines will employ the British type of spark plugs and until American manufacture of these plugs is underway British supplies will have to be depended upon. The U.S.A.A.F.have on order from Britain 100,000 RC5/2 plugs. Up to the timeof writing we have had only 124 RC5/2 plugs for engine development and flight on V1650-3 engines. We are informed, however, of the arrival of 11,000 out of the 100,000 consignment for the Air Corps order. In view of the fact that war emergency rating of + 18 lb. boost will be realised on the V1650-3 engines, the Air Corps are anxious to have the latest and most suitable type of plug. They are taking up with B.A.C. the question of supplying the balance of the 100,000 with RS5/5 types. The 300 RS5/5 despatched from the U.K. will materially assist on the Packard testing at 18 lb. and I hope that they have been consigned to me at Detroit. I heard the other day that a package of sample parts of some kind addressed to me here was unloaded in North Africa.

Packard Merlin V1650-3 engines that were eventually delivered for production aircraft were much-modified from the development examples. Many of the problems were ironed out by the time the Mustang entered service but there were recurrences of troubles that manifested themselves during the early days of flight testing, in particular those associated with the cooling system, details of which can be found in the section dealing with problems in service.

The first production P-51B was rolled out in April 1943 and deliveries commenced in June. By this time delays in engine supply meant that many aircraft had been waiting for up to six weeks for their power plants.

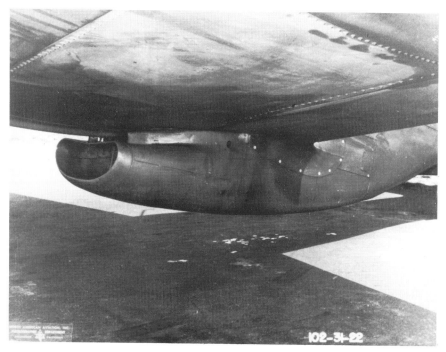

Nearly there. By the time that the first P-51Bs (type NA102 - the XP-51B was the NA101) were leaving the production line the design of the intake to the radiator duct still had not been settled. The photograph shows the original production design, soon to be modified to produce the familiar scarfed profile.

The new era

With the disposal of AL975 the era of the Mustang X at Hucknall came to an end. However, by this time production aircraft had been around and in service for two years and, not unnaturally, Hucknall had been involved in their development, and involved in more ways that one might imagine.

In appearance the production aircraft, P-51B and C models, were much improved aerodynamically. Gone was the unsightly chin radiator jutting below the spinner and in its place a much neater intake sufficient only to feed the carburettor. The radiator was re-shaped and enlarged to take into account the greater heat transfer requirements and now incorporated the intercooler matrix. Occupying a separate position in the bottom of the duct was the oil cooler, just forward of the main unit but not masking it. The whole assembly was much deeper than the original and necessitated a similar enlargement of the ventral fairing housing it. Strangely, the area of the fin remained as original despite the improvement achieved in directional stability by increasing its area. It is possible that the deepening of the central duct improved matters, though not completely as many aircraft in service were fitted with dorsal fillets as a field mod.

Proposals to fit a Griffon 61 in the Mustang came to nought as did an earlier scheme to temporarily install a Merlin 24 in order to assess the drag of the intercooler radiator by eliminating it and cleaning up the nose. The proposal to convert standard Allison-powered Mustangs on a production basis also fizzled out though the production of 500 engine installation assemblies for the scheme did get under way at Hucknall. Dorey was keen on this idea, seeing it as a means of employing his workforce in the event that Spitfire IX conversion work was curtailed. (In the event this programme continued into 1944). Should there have been a shortage of Merlin 61 engines he advocated the installation of the Merlin 28 instead. By the end of 1942 a total of fifteen conversion sets comprising engine mountings, coolant pipes and radiators had been completed along with some production tooling. The scheme was then abandoned and the suggestion that these parts be used for a further fifteen conversions, or the modification of aircraft to equip a complete squadron, came to nought also. Yet another proposal was to build aircraft from components supplied from America. Had this come about it would probably have been undertaken by Air Service Training at Hamble. It was all academic really as the delivery of complete aircraft from the USA was only six months away. For a while, though, the proposal received serious consideration, as the following memoranda reveal.

Meeting between M.A.P and Air Ministry 6 August 1942

Harriman[43] urged the RAF to accept American types of fighter to meet all overseas requirements and to supply U.S Pursuit Groups in UK with British fighters to save shipping space. It was agreed that with the approval of VCAS more Spitfires might be given to the pursuit Groups in order to persuade them to provide us with Mustang airframes which we could match with Merlin engines from British production.

Meeting between M.A.P and Air Ministry 27 August 1942

A telegram had been sent to the British Air Commission asking that the possibility of extending Mustang production in US to provide, say, 120 a month without engines for UK to be explored. If Mustang with Merlin 61 proved satisfactory the Americans might be asked to supply 200 a month for use in Middle East, India and Australia in return for equivalent number of Spitfires for US Pursuit Groups in UK. VCAS expressed doubt as to whether Spitfire IX would have good enough performance for 1943 and recommended increasing order for 1200 Merlin Mustangs to 3000 of which we should insist on a 50% share. Agreed that a further telegram be sent to BAC proposing that a definite order be placed for Mustang with Merlin 61 for the RAF.

---

[43] William Averell Harriman, US representative in London of the Combined Shipping Adjustment Board and member of the London Combined Production and Resources Board.

MEETING WITH SIR WILFRED FREEMAN AT M.A.P.
ON 25.2.43. - TO DISCUSS MERLIN - MUSTANG PRODUCTION.

Sir Wilfred Freeman opened the Meeting by asking Sir Frank Spriggs[44] whether A.S.T. would be able to tackle the assembly of Mustangs for fitting with British Merlin engines and to carry out all modifications, etc., as required. Sir Frank had with him the Manager of A.S.T., and they both confirmed that subject to the aircraft arriving built up into components, A.S.T. would be able to carry on.

Sir Wilfred then referred to a cable which he had just received from B.A.C., which stated that parts would be supplied with all machining completed but with no assemblies or sub-assemblies made up. The cable also indicated, in obscure wording, that a special technique for forming the pieces would have to be mastered by the British firm building Mustangs.

On hearing this, it was generally agreed that A.S.T.'s capacity would be inadequate, even if the whole of it was given up to the Merlin-Mustang. Sir Wilfred would not, however, agree to any interference with the programme on which A.S.T. are already working. Sir Frank Spriggs then made it clear that he had no further interest in the Merlin-Mustang project, and hoped he would be relieved of responsibility for it.

From the above it will be seen that no decision was reached regarding who is to build the aircraft. We could not, therefore, obtain an answer as to who would be responsible for the engine installation. It was, however, stated during the meeting that the aircraft pieces were going to be delivered in balanced sets complete less engine and airscrew.

C.R.D., who came to the Meeting late, was reluctant to discuss the question of the supply of an aircraft for trial installation at Hucknall, or the type of airscrew to be fitted. He therefore obtained the agreement of Sir Wilfred Freeman to defer consideration of these matters until the Meeting which C.R.D. is convening at Hucknall on Tuesday, the 2nd March.

Sir Wilfred Freeman informed the Meeting that the essential jigs and tools for building the aircraft could not be expected to arrive from America in this country before November. It appears, therefore, that even if an early decision is reached as to who is to build the aircraft; the engines will not be required for about twelve months from now, and no production of complete aircraft can be looked for much before the middle of 1944.

In view of the above, it would almost seem that the whole proposal to fit Rolls-Royce Merlin engines into Mustangs required reviewing. For instance, it seem hardly reasonable that we should be making arrangements to fit British Merlin engines into American Mustangs at about the same time as we shall be fitting American Packard engines into British Lancasters. Would it not be possible to change over the source of engine supply for the two aircraft, and in the case of the Mustang, thereby save the large amount of work called for in preparing a trial installation and making provision for the supply of the necessary Power Plant parts to suit the British engine, and, in the case of the latter, avoid the necessity for de-standardising our 'Universal' Power Plant and losing a large proportion of its claimed advantages due to the absence of an auxiliary gearbox drive on the American engine ?

---

[44] Managing Director of Hawker Siddeley Aviation of which Air Service Training was a member.

NOTES ON MEETING HELD AT ROLLS-ROYCE LIMITED HUCK-NALL, 2nd MARCH, 1943, IN RELATION TO PUTTING MERLIN 66 ENGINES INTO NORTH AMERICAN MUSTANGS TO BE BUILT IN THIS COUNTRY WITH AIRFRAME DESIGNED TO TAKE MERLIN 69 ENGINES

Prest: Mr. Schmued
        Major Hitchcock   } North American Aviation
        Mr. Legarra

        Mr. N.E.Rowe   } M.A.P.
        Mr. Walmsley

        Mr. E.W. Hives
        Mr. A.G. Elliott
        Lt. Col. Fell
        Mr. A.C. Lovesey
        Mr. W. Challier   } Rolls-Royce Limited
        Dr.E.W. Still
        Capt.R.T.Shepherd
        Mr.R.W.Harker
        Mr. J.S. Hart

GENERAL DISCUSSION ON INSTALLATION

The North American design will be different from the Mustang we have, the fuselage being increased in depth by 3" by lowering the wing by that amount. This will give a cleaner run of pipes, these being taken over the wing, whereas now they go under, giving greater flexibility for increased pipe sizes etc.

North American have run into severe corrosion troubles with the system they have been flying with Merlin 68's.[45] In Rolls-Royce experience this may be attributed to cavitation, most probably induced by the high resistance from the radiator, which had water passages about half those common in Rolls-Royce practice.

CONCLUSION 1.

The system should be designed as a pressure system i.e., a reverse of flow to that now used; this in effect puts the radiator much nearer to the pump from the standpoint of hydraulic resistance on the pressure side of the pump.

Rolls-Royce experience would point to the adoption of the conclusion stated, the use of the radiator of lower internal resistance about half that now in the North American installation in America, special attention to the run of pipe lines to avoid 'U' bends where air may be trapped, the use of copper pipes in place of aluminium pipes since the use of this material for pipes goes outside Rolls' very lengthy experience.

North American wish to retain both their high resistance radiator and their aluminium pipe lines, particularly the latter.

CONCLUSION 2.

Rolls-Royce will make an experimental test rig, full scale, as quickly as possible to simulate the production arrangements of the cooling system, to test in particular the high pressure radiator and the general run of pipe

---

[45] The mention of the Merlin 68 is misleading as this engine had different supercharger and reduction gear ratios to those of the V1650-3 and also employed a gearbox to drive the accessories. As the later V1650-7 variant corresponded to the Merlin 68, albeit without the auxiliary drive, it can be assumed that the 68 appellation was of an interim nature.

lines, to check for corrosion, and get any general information on the working of the installation. They will keep North American fully informed of the results of the work, giving interim information as they get it.

(2) North American have experienced rumbling noises at 400 mph in flight, which increase in intensity when the radiator flap is open. They have worked generally on the airframe, stiffening parts, etc., but have not yet cured the trouble. Rolls-Royce think this is a vibration effect from the radiator tubing; they have done a great deal of work on this, and will let Mr.Schmued have a copy of their report.[46]

It is most important that any advice Rolls-Royce wish to give to North American, or vice-versa, as a result of their joint experience in experimental flight should be interchanged as rapidly as possible. M.A.P. must discuss with Rolls-Royce and U.S.A. representatives ways and means of doing this.

The intention is to get a Merlin 66 to America by the quickest possible route for North American to use as a mock-up for their own installations. Special arrangements must be made, in conjunction with B.A.C., on the American side to receive the engine.

The above should be compared with memo Lr/347/MG dated 2 March 1943, the same date as the above meeting at Hucknall. It is doubtful that those at the meeting were aware of its contents which, once they were known, were probably responsible for the dropping of the scheme.

Problems in service

In June 1943 the first P-51B Merlin Mustangs began to emerge from the production lines of North American's Inglewood factory at Mines Field, now the site of Los Angeles International airport. Two months later the Dallas plant produced its first aircraft, designated P-51C but identical to the B version. Deliveries commenced to the USAAF in England in the late summer along with RAF models known as the Mustang III. As was to be expected, it was only a matter of time before examples of the production machines arrived at Hucknall for development purposes and also for investigation into the various teething problems that usually beset a new type entering service.

Oil system

The first aircraft delivered to Hucknall belonged to the latter category and was involved in the investigation into oil loss from the engine breather system, a condition which, apart from reducing the oil quantity available, a vital factor when undertaking long range escort duties, resulted in a very dirty aircraft. The aircraft concerned was a USAAF example, 43-12425 fitted with Packard Merlin V1650-3 No.B264. It arrived just 51 weeks after the first flight of the prototype Merlin powered Mustang.

---

[46] The rumbling in the radiator duct was, in fact, at its worst when the exit flap was closed and its severity caused considerable annoyance to the pilot. In an effort to understand the problem the XP-51B was sent to the Ames Aeronautical Laboratory where it was placed in the wind tunnel. Various modifications to the configuration of the duct were undertaken and the effectiveness of each was assessed by an engineer sitting in the cockpit while the wind tunnel speeds were taken up to 500 mph. The result of these tests was the extended and scarfed intake with the deeper boundary layer gutter that was later evident on all production P-51B/C/D aircraft.

```
                    FLIGHT INSTRUCTION SHEET.

                                        No. ___15_____
     From ___Chr._____ For EWS/TAS,    Date __9-9-43_____
     To ____RTS_____

     Hangar _____THG___  Airscrews _____  Liaison _____
     Instruments_____OAL___ Contract _WH & Btl____   R.T.O. Mr. Jones.____
     Project _____EWS___ D.O. _____F_____      A.I.D. Mr. Martin____
     Inspection _____Pnl___ Shops ___Tyr._____   Development ___Hks.____

     Aircraft___MUSTANG AL.975_____ Engine_Merlin 70/83335_____
     Special Units fitted_Additional rocker cover breathers. Oil collector pot.


     Previous Instructions Issued_____
     Object of Tests__To improve oil breathing system and measure oil loss
                      _____and oil consumption._____

     Specification of Tests__Climb to 25,000 ft. at 2850 R.P.M. + 12 lbs. boost.
     Full throttle level at 25,000 ft. at 3000 R.P.M. + 18 lbs. boost.
     Steep dive from 25,000 ft. to 15,000 ft.
     Full throttle level at 15,000 ft. at 3000 R.P.K. + 18 lbs. boost.
     Cruise at 2850 + lbs. boost making up an endurance of 1 hr. 30 mins.
     recording main oil pressures and oil temperatures at regular intervals.
     Check fluctuation of oil pressure with application of negative G.
     manoeuvres.

                                        Signature__Chr/RLS._____

     ROLLS-ROYCE LIMITED, HUCKNALL, NOTTS.
```

A solution to this problem proved to be no simple matter and was to involve four other Mustangs in the investigation, though one can be discounted as it was damaged in a forced landing before any worthwhile data was obtained. In the two weeks that 43-12425 spent at Hucknall the cure for the oil loss had not been found, but by coupling the rocker cover and crankcase breathers to a common pipe venting beneath the radiator duct the life of one Mustang pilot at least became a little more pleasant by not having to worry about peering though an oil soaked windscreen. The aircraft which bore the brunt of the investigation were AL975 and FX901. They were assisted for a while by FX858 and, briefly, FX852.

It soon became clear that he problem was caused by a number of factors, non of which were amenable to a simple cure. The worst of these was piston blow-by whereby combustion gases were being forced past the rings and into the crankcase thereby creating excessive pressure. The trouble manifested itself when operating at 2875 rpm or more at high boost pressures and was particularly bad at the higher altitudes. Blow-by from a typical British Merlin was 10 cu ft/min but the American Packards were producing twice this amount. The second cause was the unsuitability of the oil tank to cope with the requirements of the oil system. The air capacity of the tank was too small and this coupled with the lack of anti-frothing devices resulted in a highly aerated system.

As mentioned earlier the solution to the dirty appearance of the aircraft following oil loss was to couple a breather pipe from the rocker covers into the crankcase breather and then vent overboard beneath the radiator duct instead of separately from the engine cowling. Regarding oil loss, this was dependent on whether or not a 'good' engine was installed, i.e., an engine with low blow-by characteristics. If a 'bad' engine was installed the problem of high oil loss still remained despite the modified vent pipes; with a 'good' engine it could just cope.

A new oil tank was designed and constructed by Hucknall with a capacity of 9 1/4 gallons with 2 1/4 gallons of air space as opposed to 10.3 and 1.2 gallons respectively for the American tank. This produced 0.9 gallons of froth which was a great improvement on the original's 3 1/2 gallons. Although a 100% answer to the oil problems with Packard Merlin was not achieved during the tests undertaken at Hucknall it was recommended that for new production a redesigned breather system and oil tank be provided and until such time that a cure had been found that, where possible, to limit engine speed to 2700 rpm for the first two hours of flying.

Two RAF Mustangs IIIs were sent to Hucknall for general development work. These aircraft, FX858 and FX901, were also employed in the investigations into a number of engine complaints that had manifested themselves during the early period of service with the RAF and USAAF. These aircraft were fitted with the standard Packard V1650-3 engine about which a number of problems had been reported.

Fuel system

The mixture control on these aircraft was hand operated with a selection of four positions - full rich, for take-off only - auto rich, for operation above 30 in. Hg (+ 4 lb) boost - auto lean, for economical cruising - idle cut off, for starting and stopping. Initially it was discovered that the engine would not run in the auto rich position in FS gear. Full rich for take-off was satisfactory followed by a change to auto rich for climb at either 2850 rpm, 61 in. Hg (+ 15 lb) boost or 3000 rpm, 67 in. Hg (+ 18 lb), but with the change to FS gear at around 21,000 ft. a complete cut-out occurred followed by black smoke and a failure of the engine to keep running indicating that the mixture was too rich. Immediately the mixture control was put into auto lean normal running was obtained. All subsequent take-offs and climbs were carried out with the control locked in the auto lean position with very satisfactory results up to 38,000 ft.

There then commenced a programme whereby fuel flowmeter tests were carried out over a complete range of engine operating conditions at various altitudes in both supercharger gears. Over the cruising regime the air/fuel ratio was consistent at around 15 to 1 with a gradual richening up to 12 to 1 at 18 lb boost, this being as near ideal as could be expected. There was, though, a slight tendency to richen up at 35,000 ft indicating that the altitude capsule was reaching the limit of its correction.

The elimination of the full rich and auto rich positions on the mixture control made the carburettor operational, but the siting of the control in the cockpit still left a potential danger element in as much that when feeling for the pitch control to reduce rpm immediately after take-off, the mixture lever could be mistaken and moved from auto lean to idle cut off resulting in a dangerous

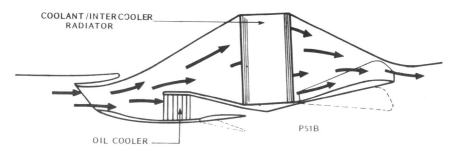

COOLANT / INTERCOOLER
RADIATOR

OIL COOLER

P51B

Cross section through the P-51B radiator duct. To cater for the increased heat transfer requirements it was deepened considerably to house the combined main and intercooler radiators and the resited oil cooler. The intake was isolated further from the fuselage to prevent the boundary layer from entering the duct and had a fixed area entry - airflow though all units being controlled by exit flaps.

Front view of the Harrison radiator. The left hand section is the intercooler matrix, the centre and right the main coolant unit. A division in the top and bottom castings sealed the two independent systems. For some reason the whole matrix assembly was paint sprayed on completion and the during the course of operation it would flake off and clog the airways between the fins and tubes. When installed in the first North American prototype the whole assembly was rotated 90 degrees giving the coolant an east/west flow with the intercooler section uppermost.

loss of power. This had, in fact, occurred with Hucknall pilots who, fortunately, realised immediately what had happened. A simple gate was produced, therefore, which bolted onto the quadrant. To put the lever from idle cut off to auto lean required a straight forward push but selection of idle cut off from auto lean meant springing the lever through the gate.

The USAAC had reported oscillation of the boost control and its failure to control satisfactorily. The problem was at its worst during combat climbs at +15 lb boost but gradually receded as boost pressure fell with altitude. Below +12 lb boost the operation was consistent and satisfactory until the supercharger changed into FS gear when the oscillation returned in a more violent manner. An uprating of the engine to +18 lb boost made matters much worse. It was considered that the problem was caused by having too small a boost control unit; the Merlin 28 type being used on a two-stage engine. Although a complete cure was not affected a considerable improvement was achieved by fitment of stronger springs in the boost aneroid and relay piston.

Cooling system

The radiator in the P-51B was an entirely different unit to that of the earlier Allison powered aircraft. Much larger in size it had to contend with greater coolant flows and temperatures and the consequent need for increased heat transfer. The whole assembly consisted of the main coolant and intercooler matrices. The oil cooler was mounted separately, just forward and in the floor of the duct. Although the waterways of the radiator matrix were of robust construction it was considered that they were too narrow, being barely half the width used in standard British practice. Service experience had shown that the tubes were prone to silting up after a short period of time resulting in prohibitively high coolant and charge temperatures, the latter causing detonation problems.

The trouble was traced to the use of American specification glycol coupled with the aforementioned aeration problem. A sample of the glycol was analysed from which it was proved that the phosphoric acid content of the inhibitor would corrode copper in thirty hours. Flight tests were undertaken with engines operating with a different inhibitor in the glycol (NaMBT) and also with British specification glycol. Coolant system modifications were also involved, mainly concerned with reducing the excessive aeration in the header tank. This was partly due to the employment of an older design of steam separator (subsequently improved). The condition was made worse by the fact that the intercooler pump had been speeded up and the flow increased from 22 gpm to 30.

A third problem affecting the cooling system was the poor seating of the header tank relief valve. This unit had a metal seating and was set to control the header tank pressure to equal the atmosphere or vapour pressure, whichever was the greater. If the temperature and altitude conditions were such that the vapour pressure was greater than the atmospheric, then the system would become unstable causing coolant to leak by the metal face at a rate in excess of two pints per hour. When this happened the coolant level fell below the outlet with the consequent increase in aeration and reduction in flow. The answer lay in a relief valve with a rubber seating as was employed on British two-stage engines. This modification was, in fact, taken up by Packard on later production engines as was the NaMBT inhibitor in the glycol.

A proposal to modify Spitfire IX type header tanks for use on the Mustang was in fact undertaken by Hucknall. However, after a great deal of misunderstanding and the inevitable procrastination, only fifty were completed by which time the war in Europe was over and nobody wanted them. In any case, it hadn't taken the Americans long to come up with a field salvage scheme which both repaired and improved the existing tanks[47].

It might be assumed by the reader that these aircraft were employed upon the investigation of one particular problem at a time. This was no so. The coolant troubles were only one aspect of a flight development programme that included the oil breather tests, sparking plug assessment and above all, performance investigation, any combination or all of which were undertaken at the same time. But in June 1945 all Mustang flight development at Hucknall

The top of the radiator matrix with the top plate removed shows the state of the unit taken from FX858 after only 22 hours of flying. The coolant used was American glycol and soft water without an inhibitor added. During this period it was common for the Hucknall Mustangs III's to be grounded so that their radiators could be flushed out to remove the accumulated silt.

---

[47] There was, in fact, a spate of header tank failures on Mustang aircraft to such an extent that the supply of spare units could not keep pace with the demand. To alleviate this problem until regular supplies were forthcoming from the USA the Spitfire header tank, suitably modified, was considered the must likely expedient. As an example the USAAF sent 43-6557 to Hucknall to be so modified.

A close-up view of the internal passages of the radiator removed from FX901 after 91 hours flying. The coolant used was English glycol with standard inhibitor. The narrowness of the waterways can be clearly seen and were only half the width of those in British radiators. The tubes were made of copper but unlike British practice they were not tinned inside their bores. Flow through the matrix as seen here was down to 68 gallons per minute from a 7 foot head of water. During a climb at +18 lb. boost the temperature of the coolant leaving the radiator was 140°C - with the matrix flushed and cleaned it was down to 105°C. The intercooler radiator was similarly affected producing a loss of 8% of intercooling. This equated to about 40 bhp and 3-4 mph. When the passages were totally free of silt the radiator had a 5% better heat dissipation than the equivalent Morris matrix.

ceased, with the exception of performance tests. Wherever possible tests were transferred to other types of aircraft. Investigations into the leading-up of sparking plugs continued with Lancaster aircraft and Corliss throttle work shifted to the Mosquito.

Performance investigation

As mentioned earlier FX858 and FX901 were delivered with the standard Packard V1650-3 engine. During their time at Hucknall they were fitted with the latest and most advanced marks of Merlin and underwent an exhaustive performance investigation programme. Strangely, these two aircraft do not appear to have undertaken a performance calibration in their standard condition. This was a standard procedure in order to assess what benefits, if any, had been achieved by the changes to the installation. Had they done so, however, there is no reason to suspect that their top speed would have been

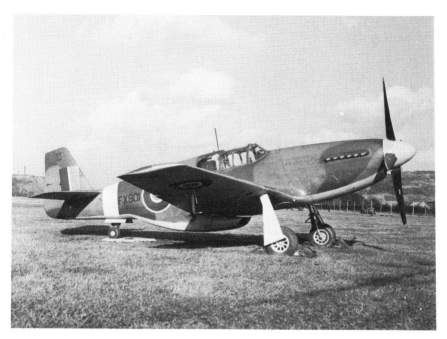

Mustang III FX901 as delivered new from Speke. Like FX858 it was initially employed on oil loss investigation and performance evaluation with high-boosted engines. Half of its career was spent evaluating the effect of high charge temperatures on the life of sparking plugs. 130, 150 and 160 octane fuel permitted the use of very high boost pressures and contained additional amounts of lead as an additive to prevent detonation. This created problems, even in transport aircraft operating on 100 octane, when deposits formed across the electrodes and shorted out the spark. High boost and low RPM was the formula for long range reliability and it was essential, therefore, to have a plug that could withstand this demanding condition.

different from the normal for the type - 437 mph at around 25,000 ft. give or take a couple either way to allow for individual airframe differences.

FX858 was fitted with Merlin RM.14.SM No.90353 (Merlin 100). This engine, capable of delivering over 2100 bhp, employed an SU fuel pump instead of a Bendix fuel injector. Test fights consisted of timed climbs and level speeds at 3000 rpm utilising + 18 lb and + 25 lb boosts. For the latter condition 150 grade fuel (RDE/F/290) was used to prevent detonation. Take-off weight was 9110 lb. At + 18 lb boost the fastest speed attained was just under 400 mph in MS gear and 451 mph at 23,100 ft in FS. With boost pressure at + 25 lb 417 mph was achieved at 4,600 ft in MS and 453 mph at 18,000 ft in FS. These speeds were attained with a .42 propellor reduction gear ratio; repeat tests with a .471 gear ratio reducing the figures by about 7 mph. The difference in speed between the two configurations at *equivalent altitudes* showed the higher boosted engine to be up to 23 mph faster at 4,600 ft in MS and a similar amount in FS at 18,000 ft.

At +25 lb boost the rate of climb (ROC) was 4780 fpm in MS at ground level to 6,800 ft and 4160 fpm in FS at 14,000 ft. This bettered the +18 lb boost figures by 720 fpm at ground level afterwhich it decreased by 140 fpm per 1000 ft of altitude until at 7,000 ft the advantage had disappeared.

FX901 was fitted with an RM.16.SM (Merlin 113), No.90351, and underwent a performance programme which was then compared with the results obtained with FX858 with Merlin 100 installed. This aircraft was heavier at 9260 lb but had a 1500 feet full throttle height advantage in that it did not have air intake gauzes fitted and thus enjoyed a 5 mph advantage at altitude. Again, operating at +25 lb boost, though with higher gear ratios, this aircraft clocked 430 mph in MS at the full throttle height of 12,000 ft and 454 mph in FS at 26,800 ft. The following table compares the performance of the two installations at various heights but not the rated altitudes (full throttle heights).

Altitude	TAS in mph		ROC in fpm		Time to Height in mins	
	100	Merlin 113	100	Merlin 113	100	Merlin 113
GL	392	381	4780	4200	-	-
5,000	412	401	4340	4200	1.05	1.2
10,000	414	422	4180	4000	2.25	2.4
20,000	445	428	3250	2960	4.85	5.3
30,000	432	453	1780	2160	8.9	8.9
36,000	410	441	900	1330	13.7	12.4

The Merlin 113, like the Merlin 100, was equipped with an SU fuel injection pump but featured the Corliss barrel-type throttle which was designed to reduce the pressure drop through the throttle box and give lighter operation. In some aircraft, particularly the Mosquito, the normal butterfly-type of throttle was extremely heavy to operate even with the friction damper slackened off.

The final performance investigation was to have been carried out by FX858, this time fitted with Merlin RM.17.SM No.90369. This odd rating, which never went into production, featured supercharger rotors of increased diameter, 12.7 and 10.7 inches as opposed to the usual 12.0 and 10.1 inches, and exhaust cams with longer duration. The gear ratios were 5.79 and 7.06, identical to the Merlin 100. It was, however, capable of operating at +30 lb boost. Unfortunately, an engine failure on its first flight necessitated a forced landing at RAF Syerston when the reduction gear pinion race stripped following a six minute level at maximum conditions. Further attempts proved fruitless and the programme came to an end when another forced landing, this time at RAF Bottesford, revealed that No.3 con-rod had failed and practically cut the engine in half. This incident, in June 1945, brought to an end all Mustang flight development at Hucknall.

Improving the breed
Although not entirely within the scope of this book, mention must be made of subsequent Mustang developments in which Rolls-Royce was directly involved. Edgar Schmued's visit to England in the Spring of 1943, culminating in his visit to Rolls-Royce, had enabled him to receive a first-hand update on the progress with the Merlin 100 series engine. Whereas British fighters had gained

Mustang III (P-51B) FX858 was Hucknall's general development aircraft. Employed initially on investigation into oil loss it spent the rest of its career on performance evaluation with high-boosted engines. Fastest speed attained was 451 MPH with the Merlin RM.14.SM installed.

most of their performance improvements by engine development and very little aerodynamically, North American were taking positive steps to see that airframe enhancement marched side by side with the greatly increased power then becoming available from the Merlin.

SECRET

Hs.
E.
Lov.
Dor/Chr.   Lp.5/LA. 12.2.43

    I saw Legarra yesterday, and he showed me a general arrangement drawing of a new Mustang for the Packard 1650/3 engine, which looked very attractive.

    The North American people had particulars of all the Spitfire weights, and these have been brought down to the smallest units, and working to the same factors as are for the Spitfire, they have evolved this new type. The factors, however, are not such as would be acceptable to the American Army Air Corps. For instance, one of their requirements apparently is that you should be able to run the engine half-throttle continuously for half an hour on the ground. There are a number of other very stiff conditions.

    Legarra is visiting Hucknall with this arrangement drawing, and I think the matter is worth further investigation, particularly bearing in mind the Merlin development projected.

    I took some rough performance figures off his curves. We have to bear in mind that they may be a little optimistic. They are as follows:-

Climb.	Speed.
4200 at sea level.	370 at sea level.
4600 at 13000.	445 at 16500.
3500 at 18000.	435 at 22000.
3400 at 23000.	455 at 27000.
500 at 43000.	
24000. 6 minutes	

The engine power available was on the same chart, and was as follows:-

Power Curve. 15-lb.

1400 B.H.P. at sea level.
1500 B.H.P. at 13000.
1200 B.H.P. at 18000.
1225 B.H.P. at 23000.
600 B.H.P. at 40000.

Total weight about 7000-lb.

It has a very good view, and would appear to be an improvement aerodynamically on the existing Mustang.

Would Chr please express an opinion on the performance quoted, and let us have a curve for 18lb boost.

Lp.1/EKB.   11th. March, 1943

Air Marshall Linnell,
Ministry of Aircraft Production,
Millbank,
LONDON. S.W.1.

Dear Air Marshall,

We have had Mr. Schmued,[48] Mr. Legarra, and Lt. Logan, of the Technical Section U.S.A.A.C. and a considerable discussion took place in regard to the lightened Mustang.

You will be aware that Mr. Hives has discussed with Sir Wilfred the question of ordering two of these lightened Mustangs from America for this country, and Mr. Schmued has had a cable from Mr. Kindelberger, in which he states that two further aircraft should be built in addition to the three ordered by the American Air Corps, providing the order is placed within one month.

Mr. Kindelberger also stated in his cable that he would be able to ship on the 1st. May, a complete engine mounting, cowl, nose spinner, as fitted to the existing Mustang with Packard Merlin, for fitting to our Mustang, in order that we can proceed along parallel lines to North American on certain installation features.

---

[48] Schmued was flown up to Hucknall by Hitchcock. The latter paid a number of visits to the airfield, flying up from Hendon in his Beechcraft UC-43 Traveler. During one such visit, on 6 November 1942, he flew AL975 thus becoming the first American to fly a Merlin Mustang. He flew it again on 21 April 1943 along with two other pilots, Mirley and Clark. Others who came to Hucknall for the same experience were W/C Finlay, Commanding Officer of the AFDU, Jeffrey Quill of Supermarines and "Mutt" Summers of Vickers Armstrong.

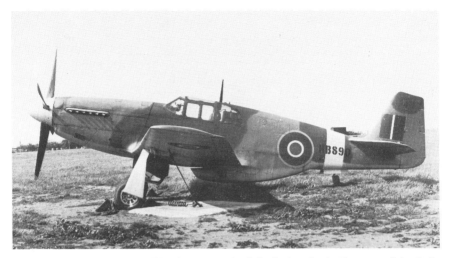

Mustang III HB890 spent all of its time at Hucknall furthering the development of the Rolls-Royce governor-controlled fuel-injection pump. The tests were mainly concerned with the fuel metering characteristics of the instrument when operating at + 25 lb boost pressures.

The only P-51D received at Hucknall was 44-14244 which came for the installation of interconnected controls. This view and that of FX901 show to advantage the definitive radiator duct fitted to all P-51B/C and D models. A dorsal fin has been fitted to improve directional stability though this problem never really went away until the advent of the tall-finned P-51H. This aircraft was fitted with a Packard V1650-7 engine which was geared for top speed at low to medium altitudes. For all its sleekness it was only 5-8 mph faster than the Mustang X.

FACTORY REPRESENTATIVE DETACHMENT
HEADQUARTERS VIII AIR FORCE SERVICE COMMAND
APO 633   U. S. ARMY

22nd March, 1943.

Dear Mr. Lappin :

    I am about to leave England, and would like to express my appreciation and thanks for the many courtesies I have had from your Company, and yourself.

    I consider myself very fortunate to have been in such close contact with you and the firm that I feel had the major share in winning the Battle of Britain. Rest assured that North American Aviation, Inc. will not fail to contribute its share towards winning this war.

    I hope I made some friends here, and if you come to America do not fail to stop at North American Aviation, Inc. If you can make it, be there August 1st.

Most sincerely yours,

EDGAR SCHMUED
CHIEF DESIGNER

W. Lappin, Esq.,
Messrs. Rolls Royce Limited,
15, Conduit Street,
London, W. 1.

Ubiquitous though he was, Lappin did not keep the rendezvous. However, Hives did and in his visit report dated 28 September 1943 he had this to say about his trip to Inglewood, Detroit and Dayton.

North American was the most refreshing visit I paid in the U.S.A. They have a very good engineering staff who are very capable. We went over a number of troubles they are having on the first production P.51 machine.

I saw the new lightened machine. My estimate is that it should be flying by the end of the year. It should be an outstanding machine. They have improved the pilot's view considerably from the original scheme. So far, they have orders for 5 of these machines - 3 for the U.S.A. and 2 for England. The anticipated production will start in September 1944. I strongly recommended that they should try and make 20 of these machines before their production is in hand.

No-one in the U.S.A. appeared to know that the requirement for fighters in this country was 25% high-altitude and 75% low-altitude.

I told them I thought that the Mustangs allocated to the R.A.F. would be criticised because they would be penalised as regards weight compared with the Spitfire, and they would be penalised on low-altitude performance because of having the equivalent of the Merlin 63 engine. Whilst I was out there this was changed, and Packards are now being instructed to produce the -7 engine, which is equivalent to our Merlin 66.

I discussed with Packard and Wright Field the method of handling Packard information. It must be realised that Wright Field has complete responsibility and control of Packards, and that Packards cannot introduce any modifications without the approval of Wright Field. There were a number of cases where modifications had been held up by Wright Field because in their opinion, based on their experience of Packard engines, they were unnecessary. I pointed out that by far the greater majority of Packard engines were being operated in England, and that it was quite wrong for Wright Field to base their information on the comparatively few P.40's which are operated by the U.S. Army Air Corps. As Wright Field must take the responsibility, therefore, I recommended that it was essential that we should have a Wright Field representative stationed at Derby, who would then be in a position to accept modifications as a result of the British tests. I found Wright Field very anxious to co-operate, and it was agreed that they should send a representative.

Taking shape on the drawing boards at Inglewood was a new model of the Mustang, the XP-51F. By paying close attention to every aspect of weight reduction North American was able to reduce the empty weight by half a ton when compared with the then current production model, the P-51D.

Lp.1/JMP   23rd March 1943.

P. H. Legarra, Esq.,
North American Aviation Inc.,
St. John's House,
Smith Square,
London, S.W.1.

Dear Legarra,

Firstly, many thanks for the pleasant meal on Friday last. I regret I had to leave early, but I fear I am much too old for getting to bed at 4 o'clock in the morning these days.

I would like to remind you that you promised when Mr. Schmued left, to let me have the specification of the light weight fighter. I want this for reference purposes, as it will be necessary in the intervening months to keep the job alive in various quarters.

It has been a most valuable thing to have Schmued visit us, and after meeting him a few times, one has no difficulty in realising why the Mustang is a good aeroplane.

E.
c. Lov.
c. Dor.   Lp.13/JMP. 30.3.44.

During a conversation I had with Louis Wait[49] of North American Aviation, he mentioned that they had achieved a reduction in weight of 1290 lb. on the lightened Mustang as compared with the existing Mustang. He also mentioned that he had flown a machine with a Simmonds control, and he expressed satisfaction with the 'dead beat' operation of this control.

---

[49] Louis S Wait, North American test pilot, visited Derby on 28 March 1944 along with Col. Cass S Hough of the Air Technical Section, 8th Army Air Force and Philip Legarra. He is not to be confused with L L Waite, head of Technical Engineering at NAA. Cass Hough later became Bill Lappin's son-in-law.

Attention: E. W. Hives Esq. C.H.

I have just returned from a visit to Los Angeles in company with Macdonald and I am setting forth here my impressions of the contacts I made at the Douglas Aircraft Company, Inc. at Santa Monica, and also with North American Aviation, Inc. at Inglewood.

May I say that a week spent at the Beverly Hills Hotel was enough to show us why it was always fairly easy to persuade Lr. that it was "about time he paid another visit to the West Coast."

NORTH AMERICAN

The main reason for my visit to North American was to see the progress which has been made with regard to the installation of the two RM.14.SM engines which you have sent there. However, I had a good look around the plant as well, both from a general interest point of view and also with the idea of cooperating with Macdonald in his investigation of inspectional and other troubles which occur on Packard built Merlin engines after they leave this plant. The observations which we made under this latter heading will, we feel, be of considerable use to us when we get involved in arguments at the Packard Alteration Committee Meetings with regard to engine troubles in service.

I also had general discussions with the North American Engineering Department and contacted Mr. Rice, Chief Engineer, J. W. Young, Messrs. Wheeler and Beerer, and others. I also, of course, met Mr. Schmued, Chief Designer.

I was getting a bit confused myself with the various varieties of P-51 aircraft, and I think I will therefore put in here a list of the different models as at present being built or contemplated.

P-51B is the first standard production machine with V-1650/3 engine.
P-51C is the same machine built at Dallas.
P-51D has a V-1650/7 engine.
P-51H will have the V-1650/9 engine.
XP-51F is the lightened machine having a V-1650/3 engine.
XP-51G are the two machines fitted with the RM.14.SM engines.

In addition there is the XP-82 which is the twin engined machine now under consideration which will have a V-1650/9 or /11 engine on one side, and the V-1650/21 engine (opposite rotation) on the other side.

RM.14.SM

I got the impression that they were not now so interested in flying the RM.14.SM engines as they would have been had these engines been made available to them some months earlier. The reason for this is that they are not contemplating making any production machines with your engines but that the corresponding P-51H machines with the V-1650/9 engines will, of course, be installationally somewhat different, and seeing that they expect to get some V-1650/9 engines before the end of the year for their prototype flying, the XP-51G machines will probably not be of as much use to them as they might have been. The first machine will not be ready to fly for about three weeks, whereas the second one will not be ready until some time later. In any case, they do not propose to fly either machine until they have had some tests on one engine in order to find how the ratings of the engine compare with its British ratings when using the available American grade 150 fuel.

I had an interesting talk with Mr. W. Templeton who is, of course the Rotol representative who was sent out recently on this job. It appeared to me that it was rather lucky that he arrived on the scene when he did because he is the only person apparently who has had any connection with this job who knew how to adjust the Merlin 66 type of boost control with which these engines are fitted, and Lr. will know enough about North American to know what I mean when I say that anything which can be taken to pieces is liable to be pounced upon as soon as it enters the Inglewood factory.

It is the intention to fly the first machine, first with an Aero Products propeller and then with one of the Rotol propellers, in order to obtain a direct comparison between the two, but Templeton has not as yet unpacked any of his Rotol propellers as he does not feel it desirable to have them laying around the shop to get damaged as they evidently will not be required for some little time yet.

They tell me that they are expecting two more RM.14.SM engines in the very near future, one of which is to be sent direct to Inglewood and the other to Wright Field for altitude chamber tests, and it seemed to me that there was going to be a tendency for the North American flight tests to hang fire until they got this third engine, so that it could be used for ground tests.

XP-51F

I had a good look at one of the XP-51F machines which are the first lightened versions having the V-1650/3 engine, the reason for using the V-1650/3 engines being that the V-1650/9 is now going to have the high supercharger gear ratios. This machine incorporates the oil system and aftercooler heat exchanger with its combined aftercooler radiator and oil cooler radiator. It also incorporates the North American style of rocker cover breathers which differ considerably from the RM.14.SM arrangement. The oil heat exchanger certainly appears on the face of it to make rather a neat installation and so far is stated to be functioning very well. The one I inspected was of a somewhat temporary nature and the pipe work was not quite up to the usual North American standard. The aftercooler and oil cooler radiator is, of course, quite big and enclosed with this letter I am giving a list of the various radiator sizes which will be of interest to you. This radiator of course is mounted behind the main engine radiator in the same duct.

In order to make the two RM.14.SM engines suitable for installation in the XP-51G aircraft, quite a few external installational modifications had to be made and these were carried out by the Packard representative Mr. Freeman and I am enclosing a list of the modifications he carried out. I am including this list as a matter of interest but it may not be entirely comprehensible to you since reference is made to North American drawings which in a good many cases are not available to you, but you will get the general idea.

When Mr. J. W. Wheeler came over he brought with him, addressed to Psn's attention, a curve showing the performance of Mustang FX-858 with RM.14.SM engine No.90353 in it.

I took this curve with me and Mr. Schmued was very surprised to see it as he stated that the performance shown therein was very poor, particularly with regard to maximum speeds which only come to about 445 true air speed at 17,600 ft in high gear at 25lbs boost. He says he is hoping for at least 500 although of course he realised that this particular Mustang is not of the lightened variety.

E. N. Soar

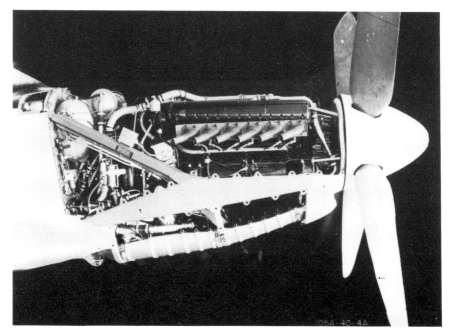

The RM.14.SM installation in the XP-51G. This shows well the cylindrical shaped oil cooler in front of the oil tank mounted on the bulkhead. In this arrangement the oil was cooled by the circulation of the intercooler coolant around the oil passages through the unit, thus negating the need for the air cooled matrix in the radiator air scoop. The XP-51F also employed this method as did the P-51H though Rolls-Royce preferred the utilisation of the main circuit. The drawback with the above system was that damage to the intercooler circuit would result in the eventual loss of the engine through lack of oil cooling whereas normally the engine would run satisfactorily in MS gear if intercooling was lost. Damage to the main coolant lines was academic as this would eventually stop the engine anyway. In the lightweight Mustangs the coolant header tank was repositioned in the fuselage above the radiator to save weight and improve weight distribution.

Top speed was 466 mph, some 30 mph faster, and it was more than two minutes quicker to 20,000 feet. The engine was the standard Packard V1650-3 as fitted to the production P-51B. This aircraft flew in February 1944 and in the following August an even lighter version, the XP-51G, appeared. Top speed of this variant was 495 mph. Power was provided by a special version of the RM.14.SM giving just over 2000 bhp. Neither of these two experimental marks saw production but the experience gained from them resulted in the fastest of all production Mustangs, the P-51H. Just too late to see war service it was powered by the Packard V1650-9 which was a version of the -7 featuring water methanol injection to boost the maximum output to 2200 bhp at 10,200 feet and giving a top speed of over 480 mph.

The ending of hostilities in Europe brought to an end one of Hucknall's most interesting and successful chapters in more ways than one. Up until now our story has concentrated upon the development of the Mustang from that of an aircraft with a moderate performance to one whereby its great potential was fully realised. By 1945 the Eighth Air Force was flying its P-51Ds on escort missions involving round trips of up to 1200 miles and endurances surpassing seven hours. Not only was this a tribute to machine but also to men who, in their noisy, cramped cockpits, owed their survival to the reliability of the single engine in front of them. There must have been many a Luftwaffe pilot astonished to find that his adversary was flying a single-engined fighter deep into the heartland of Germany all the way from England.

The Flying Test Bed

The early months of 1945 saw the termination of what was potentially the most exciting project involving Hucknall and the Mustang. The Installation Design Department had, since its inception, striven to perfect the art of installing engines in airframes in such a way that drag was reduced to an absolute minimum. By late 1942 it had gone about as far as it could with conventional installations, be they applied to fuselage or wing configurations. Thoughts were now concentrating on the buried installation whereby the engine is contained within the normal structure and not appended to it.

Like most bright ideas it had been done before, indeed Rolls-Royce had done it in the mid thirties when it had collaborated with Westlands on the F7/30 biplane fighter which flew with an evaporatively-cooled Goshawk installed midships behind the pilot. Transmission to the propeller was via a shaft, the whole arrangement affording the pilot an excellent field of vision over the nose. In contemporary times there was no one with more experience than the Bell Aircraft company who had their Airacobra flying in 1939 and who were now turning them out, along with the more advanced Kingcobra variant, by the thousand, all powered by the Allison liquid-cooled V-12 in-line engine. The time was now right for Rolls-Royce to proceed along similar lines.

The benefits were considerable. By installing the engine over the wing centre-section the two centres of gravity became one, allowing any changeover from one type of engine to another to be simplicity itself. With regard to aircraft handling, the inertia effect of the engine mass would be reduced to a minimum during pitch and yaw. From the pilot's point of view, literally, the shortened nose allowed him a forward vision unattainable with contemporary nose-engined aircraft.

The origin of the project had a link, albeit tenuous, with a couple of Miles projects of 1942. In September of that year they were considering three possible designs to meet an Air Staff requirement for a low-altitude ground attack aircraft. The first two were of conventional twin-engine layout but the third involved a radical concept in aerodynamics whereby the tailplane and elevators were repositioned in front of the wing in a canard configuration. The wing itself was moved to the rear of the fuselage. The name of Libellula was given to this concept. Miles approached Rolls-Royce for details of the Griffon engine

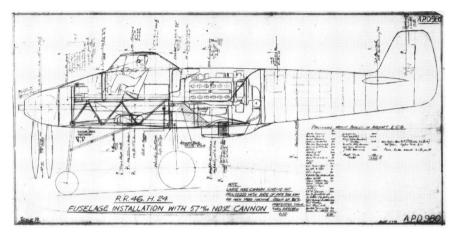

The earliest scheme showing the Company's proposal for a rear engined fighter aircraft. It is dated 17 August 1942 and has no allegience to the Mustang. The engine is the 46 litre, 24 cylinder H configuration Eagle, rated at 3000 bhp. Armament consisted of a 57mm cannon firing through the spinner and four 20mm cannons in the wing or fuselage firing through the propellor disc (this must have been tricky with contra-rotating airscrews!). The tricycle undercarriage allowed for 12 feet diameter airscrews. All-up-weight in fighting trim was 12,240 lb and length was around 34 feet. The drawing's annotations, though unreadable here, have not been deleted in order to retain originality.

and revealed that the installation would be a pusher with the propeller being driven from the engine by an extension shaft, albeit a short one.

They were supplied with the specification for the Griffon IIB and shortly after a meeting was arranged with the Controller for Research and Development, Air Marshal Linnell. He expressed an interest in the project, not only as a ground attack aircraft but as a medium-altitude fighter. In the latter role he suggested the incorporation of the Rolls-Royce two-stroke power-plant. This engine was the PI-26 Crecy and to Miles' request for details they were told that it had not reached the stage whereby a useful specification could be compiled. Nothing more was heard of the project as Miles, fearing rejection by the Air Ministry, decided to submit a more conventional design instead. The following month Miles, who were still operating under the name of Phillips and Powis, were back at Derby.

To - Hs

c.Sg.
c.Rg.
c.Lp.
c.Dor.   Wd.1/AA.27.10.42.

AIRCRAFT FOR R.R.26.P.I. 2-STROKE ENGINE

Mr Miles and Mr Brown of Phillips and Powis visited Derby on the 27th inst. to discuss the design and manufacture of a test aircraft for the R.R. 2-stroke engine. After consideration of their novel single engine and twin engine rear wing types of aircraft the following decisions were made.

1) They would immediately look into the design of a flying test bed of conventional type using standard components were possible; the aircraft to be single engine, 2 seater, with provision for a thrust augmenter similar to the arrangement proposed by Rg. or for plain exhaust jets.

2) The design of their special 2 engine tractor rear wing aircraft is more adaptable for the 2-stroke engine and its exhaust utilisation than the single engine pusher rear wing aircraft. Mr Miles will raise with M.A.P. the desirability of preparing designs of the twin engine aircraft for the 2-stroke engine in preference to the single engine aircraft.

3) They will continue the design of the single engine aircraft for the Merlin 32 engine with the view that after development of the aircraft and of the the thrust augmenter for the 2-stroke the latter can replace the Merlin, the exchange being simplified if no airscrew is fitted to the 2-stroke engine so that there will be no interference between the jets and the airscrew disc.

With regard to (1) Mr Miles anticipates being able to forward preliminary drawings by November 1st. The engine performance given to him was based on 15 lbs. boost at 2750 r.p.m. up to 15,000 ft. which on the Mk. II engine represents approx. 1750 B.H.P. take-off and 1600 at 15,000 ft. (excluding exhaust jet thrust).

Wd.

The above memo is interesting in that the first proposal mentions the use of 'standard components where possible'. This type was given the designation Miles M.46. The design of the third proposal is a little vague but seems to be referring to the original Libellula aircraft with the pusher installation, though the suggestion that propulsion be by jet thrust alone seems a little naive.

The M.46 was conventional in design and featured Mustang wings and tailplane. The engine was mounted in the nose and the afflux from the augmenter discharged via a jetpipe at the rear of the fuselage. In appearance it somewhat resembled the later Ryan Fireball mixed-propulsion naval fighter. The proposal was submitted to the Ministry and although Linnell and Sir Wilfrid Freeman were favourably disposed towards the idea the Director of Technical Development wasn't and yet another Miles design was rejected. The failure at Reading, however, did nothing to dampen the spirits at Hucknall, where among the various engines projected for development was a shaft-drive 2-stroke with a thrust augmenter fitted into a flying test bed with Mustang wings.

Reverting to the Rolls-Royce project, conversion of an existing airframe was out of the question for although the Airacobra was amenable to such a modification the Company was looking for aerodynamic advantages because this was not going to be just another flying test bed; this was going to be a fighter. Right from the start Rolls-Royce had favoured the Mustang and a number of factors had dictated that this airframe should be the basis for the design.

For a start, resourceful as Hucknall was, it did not have the experience of designing aircraft from a clean sheet of paper. Nor did it have the important ingredient of time for the proposal was to achieve a first-flight during the summer of 1943. Its recent experience of converting the Mustang to take the Merlin had given the design team an insight into its advanced aerodynamic

S E C R E T
SB.39740

D.T.D.

29th December, 1942.

Dear Sirs,

With reference to your letter of
24th December, 1942, you sent to C.R.D. prints
of provisional drawings Nos.M.46/1 and M.46/2
showing schematically a layout for a test bed
aeroplane with the Rolls-Royce P.1.26.

I must inform you that there is no
present intention to build a special test bed
aircraft for this engine and we do not wish you
to do any further work on the schematic layout
you have put forward.

Yours faithfully,

M.E.Rowe.

Director of Technical Development.

Phillips & Powis Ltd.,
The Aerodrome,
Reading,
Berkshire.

qualities and, it was thought, by utilising essential parts 'off the shelf' a great
deal of time could be saved. These parts were the wings and empennage, both
areas which traditionally require a lot of development time, particularly in the
wind tunnel. This would leave Hucknall to design a fuselage to accommodate
the rear-mounted engine and the pilot's cockpit.

The Mustang wing was one of the most advanced then in production, having
a section with the maximum thickness well back on the chord which resulted
in laminar flow to a transition point much further aft than usual. Its
construction was very robust allowing operation at weights of over 10,000 lb. The
undercarriage also contained many desirable features such as a wide track and
doors that completely enclosed the wheels. The pick-ups were located forward
of the front spar web to bring the struts well forward in relation the centre of
gravity and enabling the brakes to be used powerfully during landing. The
empennage consisted of the fin, rudder, tailplane and elevators and, most
important of all, the rear fuselage to which they were all attached.

The project started to move in January 1943 and flourished under the title
of Fighter Aircraft Proposal (Hucknall P.V.) Right from the start it was
designed around the two-stage Griffon 61 engine, then in its early stages of

development from which it was expected to emerge with an output of 2500 bhp.

At this rating and with an aircraft auw of 9400 lb the power loading would be 3.76 lb/hp, which compared with 4.67 lb/hp for the Spitfire IX and 5.3 lb/hp for the Focke-Wulf Fw190. However, it was obvious that the engine would not be developed to this state in time so for the preliminary tests a Merlin 61 was chosen which, by this time was approaching the 2000 bhp mark. This would bring the auw down to 8950 lb and the power loading up to 4.47 lb/hp.

Modifications to the engine were considerable. The propeller reduction gear was eliminated and replaced by a spur gear driving an identical one splined on to a shaft and rotating opposite to crankshaft direction. The shaft then proceded forward within a torque tube which ran through a trough in the cockpit floor between the pilot's feet and then splined into the rear of the repositioned reduction gear in the nose. The torque tube was itself splined at both ends and transmitted the torque reaction from the reduction gear case directly back to the engine, (a feature not incorporated in the Westland F7/30), and was capable of absorbing slight rotational deflections. This design feature was especially beneficial as the forward fuselage monocoque was of light construction because of the lack of engine mass. For ease of accessibility many of the units mounted on the rear of the engine were transferred to this structure and their access panels naturally robbed it of some of its rigidity.

These units, driven from the reduction gear, were the constant speed unit, generator, hydraulic and vacuum pumps and air compressor. Other items such as radio, oxygen and electric equipment were also repositioned from their traditional rear-fuselage mounting to the forward fuselage to provide ease of access. Contra-rotating airscrews were finding favour at this time and a Rotol pair eleven feet in diameter was chosen to provide propulsion.

It was anticipated that the production Mustang would standardise on cannon armament consisting of two guns in each wing, just like the Allison-engined Mustang 1A then in service. With no engine up front it was relatively simple to permit installation of a 20 mm cannon firing through the spinner thus negating a need for the two outer guns. In the event all Mustangs were equipped with .50 calibre machine guns. The specification was completed by the installation of full armour protection and special magnesium alloy bulletproof fuel tanks.

Work got underway not only in the D.O. but also in an annexe to the Anglo Plauen[50] hangar where a mock-up was constructed. To assist in its construction a complete wing assembly and empennage of a Mustang was utilised and mated to a wood and paper fuselage - the whole assembly giving a good idea of what the shape of the finished job would look like. This mock-up was later to receive a Merlin engine as no Griffon was then available. In this form it was inspected

---

[50] Anglo Plauen was a lace manufacturer who had occupied a Hangar at Hucknall before the outbreak of war. The business was suspended on the outbreak of hostilities and the hangar taken over by Rolls-Royce. It had underfloor heating and had been employed as the dope shop during the Hurricane repair campaign at the time of the Battle of Britain in 1940. Anglo Plauen returned after the war and remained until the 1960s.

Two artistic impressions, drawn in October 1943, of what the private venture fighter would look like in service. These sketches were probably prepared to show what a converted Mustang would look like and in particular the benefits to maintenance of the centre engine philosophy. The armament appears to lack cannon but retains the .5 inch calibre wing guns.

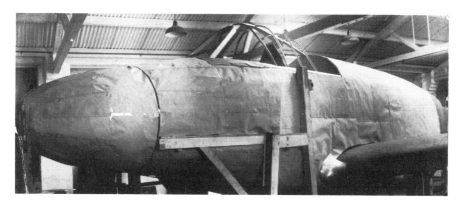

The first mock-up of the Flying Test Bed. Made from wood and paper it was matched to genuine Mustang wings and rear fuselage. It is seen here in the annex to the Anglo Plauen hangar, entry to which was only allowed to those working on the project.

by officials of the Ministry of Aircraft Production. At this stage the project was still a private venture.

Preliminary performance figures with a Griffon 71 installed were calculated about this time and showed a top speed in MS gear of 403 mph at 4800 ft and 451 mph at 20,400 ft in FS. Boost pressure in each case was + 18 lb.

Another view of the FTB mock-up. Subsequent to these pictures being taken it was further modified to enable a Merlin engine to be positioned within its centre section and as such was shown to officers of the Ministry of Aircraft Production.

Little or nothing appears to remain on file of these early months of the project but by the summer the aircraft was no nearer flight than it had been in January. The ministerial visit, though, had not been wasted and the suggestion was launched that three aircraft should be constructed as flying test beds only. The fighter idea was now a dead duck.

In June 1943 Rolls-Royce presented the Ministry of Aircraft Production with its cost estimates for three flying test beds powered by Giffon 65 Specials. The construction of each would employ the aforementioned Mustang components. The first aircraft would cost £35,000, the second and third £25,000 each. To this would be added a further £3,500 per aircraft for Rotol contra-rotating airscrews and their constant speed units. Finally, a sum of £5,500 was quoted for a mock-up and wind tunnel model. The Ministry agreed and issued Instructions to Proceed on 12 November 1943, although work on the mock-up had commenced on 1 November.

To provide the three sets of wings and empennage for the test beds the Ministry allocated three surplus Mustang 1 aircraft AL960, AM148 and AM245, which were duly dismantled to provide these parts along with other bits and pieces such as rudder pedals etc.

The mock-up was no crude affair and was built in aluminium to fine limits, indeed on its completion exactly one year later it looked to its beholder just like the real thing. It had been decided from the beginning to produce a fully-engineered model that would reduce installation problems to a minimum by enabling the positioning of such things as pipe and control runs and other items to be accurately assessed thus easing the manufacture of the aircraft proper. This it did, but raised the mock-up's price to £15,000.

The Royal Aircraft Establishment at Farnborough became involved and undertook the preliminary wind tunnel testing with a 1/10 scale model. Their tests indicated that the tailplane area should be increased by 60% and, because of the high solidity of the wash from the contra-props, the fin area should also be increased. None of these recommendations were implemented on the mock-up but it was decided that the first aircraft would feature a Tempest tail unit and one was accordingly delivered. It was also suggested by the RAE that the aircraft be stressed to permit a minimum of flying restrictions on its operation so as not to compromise its usefulness in installation testing.

It was obvious by the time taken to produce the mock-up that the job was not receiving any kind of priority status. By the turn of the year the war front was extending inexorably towards Germany and the end of hostilities was in sight. On the technical front events were, if anything, advancing even faster. Development and production of the gas turbine was well advanced; indeed, aircraft thus powered were actually in service. Just around the corner the Company was about to reveal its Nene engine which, giving 5000 lb of thrust, roughly equating to 5000 hp, for a very manageable weight and size, would create a whole new concept for installation engineers and aerodynamicists alike. It was a concept they were to relish. Indeed, the autumn would see the Nene-powered Lockheed Shooting Star at Hucknall whose sleekness in design was pure science fiction when compared with its drag encumbered contempories.

Griffon 75 Special, No. 1262 as modified to suit the Flying Test Bed's rear engine configuration. A second engine, No.1298, was also employed. Shown to advantage is the new casting arrangement to replace the original reduction gear. The propellor drive is now below the crankshaft instead of above it and the upper half of casting serves only to blank off the original reduction gear housing and the attendant accessory drives, these being transferred to the nose of the aircraft and driven by the shaft. As seen here the engine does not have the supercharger or intercooler attached. In the background can be seen the rear fuselage from one of the three Mustangs dismantled to provide parts for the project.

No more propellors, no more radiators and oil coolers and no more exhaust systems. No more trying to force even more volatile fuels into cylinders at even greater pressures. The writing was on the wall for the piston aero-engine. Its death would be a lingering one but for the Flying Test Bed mercy was at hand. On 28 February 1945 it was decided that the contract be terminated and thus end one of the more interesting chapters in the first decade of Hucknall.

There had been plans to employ the three test beds in a variety of exciting installation ventures which, had they reached fruition, would have provided the perfect swansong for propeller-driven experimental aircraft. They would have even crossed the boundary into gas turbine development. A number of actual components for the first aircraft had been completed, such as cockpit and forward fuselage, engine mounting, shaft and torque tube, hood and other

A close-up showing engine No.1262 installed in the second mock-up aircraft. The tubular cradle within which the engine was attached was part of the fuselage structure and gave the strength and rigidity formally provided by a completely monocoque fuselage. The teardrop canopy is not identifiable with any contemporary production aircraft and so must be assumed to have been specially made for the FTB.

bits and pieces. In all, the expenditure came to £11,000 plus, of course, the mock-up cost. By September the last rites had been performed and Dorey's Delusion, as someone once called it, passed into history.

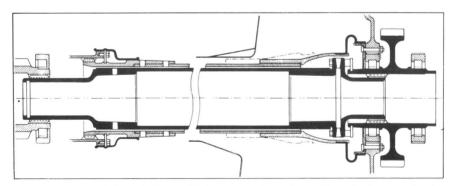

Cross section through drive shaft assembly between engine and propellor reduction gear showing the torque tube through which torsional loads from the reduction gear housing were absorbed.

Two of the actual pieces of hardware for the first flying prototype are seen in these photographs. Above is the forward fuselage and cockpit monocoque showing the heavily strengthened forward area into which the reduction gear and the accessory drives were housed. The lower picture shows the underside of the cockpit floor and clearly depicts the tunnel through which the shaft traversed between engine and reduction gear. The bulges gave clearance for the pilot's feet when operating the rudder pedals.

The final photographs taken of the FTB mock-up, now transferred to Number 6 hangar, show it in its final state before the project was terminated. A point of interest is the redesigned radiator intake which has a raked appearance similar to that of the P-51B, though no effort has been made to improve the boundary layer conditions above it. The beautiful contour of the nose is reminiscent of the Allison installation. Although a Tempest tail was obtained for the flight prototype it was never fitted to the mock-up. The high standard of engineering employed on its construction is evident and one could be forgiven for believing that it was, in fact, the real thing.

In 1945 Hucknall commissioned its 7ft x 5ft low speed wind tunnel. The model still survives. The first model to be aerodynamically tested in its working section was a scale model of the Flying Test Bed. It was suspended upside down, this photograph being inverted for convenience.

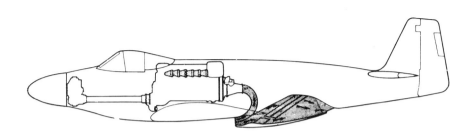

GRIFFON 61 ENGINE WITH SIMPLE EJECTOR EXHAUST

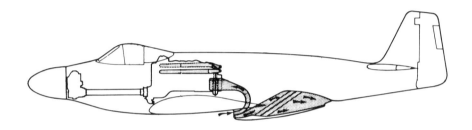

P. I. ENGINE WITH SIMPLE EJECTOR EXHAUST

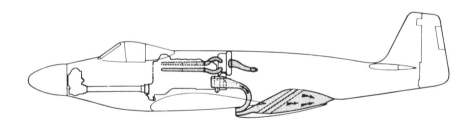

P. I. ENGINE WITH EXHAUST CRANKSHAFT-TURBINE AUGMENTER

Had the three Flying Test Beds been completed it is more than likely that only the first one would have been powered by the Griffon engine. Of the remaining two it is certain that one would have had the petrol injection, 26 litre, PI-26 Crecy engine installed. This remarkable engine, being a two-stroke, produced twice as many exhaust puffs as a conventional power plant and as a consequence, when flying fast and high, over 35% of the engine's power would have come from exhaust thrust. These three early schemes show the Griffon and Crecy installations with conventional ejector exhausts, and the Crecy with an exhaust driven turbine, the energy from which was not used for supercharging but transferred to the propellor drive - in this case via the crankshaft.

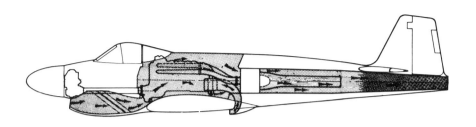

P.I. ENGINE WITH SEPARATE EXHAUST THRUST AUGMENTER

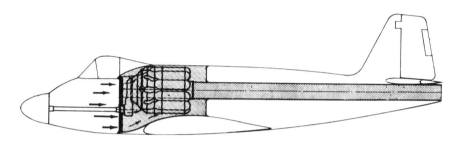

W. 2. B

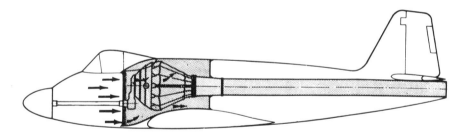

B. 37.

Three more variations on the Flying Test Bed theme. The first employs an exhaust driven turbine, the gases from which also produce jet thrust whereby the unburnt fuel within the jet is ignited and mixed with excess air under pressure. Such a scheme would have been the ultimate answer to the utilisation of the exhaust for thrust. The weight of the turbine unit required the resiting of the radiator beneath the nose with the consequent redeployment of the electrical and other equipment. It is something of a paradox that the very cause of the demise of the FTB concept, the gas turbine engine, was also considered as a suitable propulsive power. In each case, though, it would have driven an airscrew in a manner later employed with the first Trent engine. All three configurations would have required a complete redesign of the rear fuselage and tail.

Blair's Excalibur
And finally, the story would not be complete without mention of the visit to Hucknall of *Excalibur III*. Charles F Blair was a senior captain for Pan American World Airways and one of the most honoured pilots of his time. In 1950 he purchased the P-51 in which Paul Mantz had won the Bendix Trophy in 1946 and 1947. With this aircraft, powered by a Packard V1650-9, he was to create a record which stands to this day; the fastest transatlantic crossing by a piston-engined aircraft.

Apart from attempting a record Blair had a secondary purpose in experiencing the then relatively unknown phenomenon known as the jetstream. By flying in these high velocity westerly winds at 37,000 ft he was able to complete the New York to London Heathrow flight at an elapsed time of 7 hours 48 mins. The 3473 statute miles were covered at an average speed of 446 mph on 31 January 1951. The same journey today by Boeing 747 is but one hour quicker.

In the following May he undertook a flight from Bardufoss in Norway to Fairbanks, Alaska. This was the first solo flight over the Arctic and North Pole and the first by a single-engined aircraft. The flight served as an evaluation of a navigation system that he had developed for flying in polar regions. The 3260 mile flight took 10 hours 27 mins. In preparation for this journey he flew *Excalibur III* to Hucknall on 21 May for a check over.

By all accounts the standard of the modifications previously undertaken were not compatible with flying the Atlantic in a single-engined aircraft and expecting to arrive. That it did and got back was a tribute to the faith of pilot in machine. Examination revealed a number of leaks from the various fuel tanks though this was not surprising when one considers the amount of fuel required for such a journey and the problem of installing the auxiliary tanks to contain it.

The magnetos were checked, tappets adjusted and oil system serviced. The coolant system was flushed and replenished and Dunlop even chipped in with a new main wheel inner-tube. On 23 May *Excalibur* was flown to Heathrow and Hucknall's association with the Mustang finally ended.

Captain Charles F Blair

APPENDIX I

The Aircraft

This listing gives all Mustangs that were taken on charge at Hucknall. It shows all movement dates, engines installed, development details and time flown (hrs.mins), and the contract numbers to which it was all charged. The contracts were terminated when the allotted flying hours were used up (a Merlin flight development contract often covered a variety of aircraft types), after which another was issued. Contract lives varied from 100 to over 1000 hours. B.118479/40 was a contract to cover miscellaneous Merlin and Allison flying to a total of 200 hours. Engines 2073 was for 150 hours of Mustang flight development which in time was replaced by Engines 2832 for a further 200 hours.

AG518
Arrived 29 May 1942 from Lockheed Aircraft Corporation, Speke.
Allison V1710 F3R No.6543

Contract: 993704/39   General performance calibration (12.15)
                           Pattern airframe to provide details for
                           Merlin conversions (Contract B.118479/40)
                           Test flight following re-assembly (0.35)

Desptached 28 July 1942 to 12MU Kirkbride.

AL960
Arrived 7 June 1943 from 51MU Lichfield.
Allison V1710 F3R No.6664

Contract: SB27058   Dismantled to provide parts for rear-
                           engined Flying Test Bed. Project cancelled.

Struck off Rolls-Royce charge 4 May 1944.

AL963
Arrived 26 June 1942 from Lockheed Aircraft Corporation, Speke.
Allison V1710 F3R No.6716

Contract: 993704/39   General performance calibration (3.30)
        B.118479/40   Completion of performance calibration (0.45)
                           Conversion to Merlin installation

Merlin 65 No.82459
Contract: Engs 2073   First flight after conversion 21 January 1943
                           Installation and handling trials (1.40)

Despatched 26 January 1943 to AFDU Duxford. Returned next day.
Despatched 28 January 1943 to AFDU Duxford.
Returned to Hucknall 3 February 1943 for fitment of dorsal fin.
Despatched 12 February 1943 to AFDU Duxford.
Returned to Hucknall 26 February 1943.

Merlin 65 No.82551	General performance calibration (10.15) Endurance testing of the SU Mk.II single-point fuel injection pump (34.20) Heat transfer investigation (1.10)
Merlin 66 No.156369	General performance investigation (1.00) Heat transfer investigation (3.15)
Contract: Engs 2832	Performance investigation at + 18 lb boost with series intercooler radiator (4.20)
Merlin 65 No.82551	Endurance testing of SU Mk.II single-point fuel injection pump (44.55)

Despatched 18 November 1944, by road, to Messrs Air Spares Ltd. Hyde, Cheshire

AL975
Arrived 27 June 1942 from Lockheed Aircraft Corporation, Speke.
Allison V1710 F3R No.6683

Contract: 993704/39	General performance calibration (4.25)
B.118479/40	Conversion to Merlin installation.
Merlin 65 No.721 Contract: Engs 2073	First flight after conversion to 13 October 1942 Installation and handling trials (2.50) General performance calibration (11.15) Fuel system investigation (2.00)
Merlin 65 No.82445	Handling tests following fitment of dorsal fin (4.25) General performance calibration (8.10) Heat transfer investigation (1.50) Fuel system investigation (3.00)
Merlin 70 No.83335	Installation and handling tests with extended fin leading edge (5.15) General performance calibration (18.30) Heat transfer investigation (6.35) Engine breather loss investigation (10.15)

Despatched 1 April 1943 to AFDU Wittering.
Returned to Hucknall 6 April 1943.

Contract: Engs 2832	Shunt cooling system trials (18.25) Engine breather loss investigation (6.05) Investigation into cutting out (2.25) Evaluation of Stromberg 8D44/4 carb. (7.55)

Merlin 71 No.83025   Shunt cooling system reliability flying
and endurance testing of SU fuel pump (68.55)
Radiator suitability tests with shunt
cooling system (2.00)

Contract: Engs 4086   Continuation of shunt cooling reliability
flying (18.45)

Force landed 14 March 1945, due to engine failure, at Fradswell, near Uttoxeter.

Despatched March 1945, by road, to Messrs Air Spares Ltd. Hyde, Cheshire.

AM121

Arrived 7 June 1942 from Lockheed Aircraft Corporation, Speke.

Allison V1710 F3R No.6732

Contract: 993704/39   General performance calibration (8.35)
Calibration of radiator duct efficiency (3.20)

Contract: B.118479/40   Completion of performance calibration and
radiator duct efficiency tests (12.15)
To workshops 15 November 1942 for conversion
to Merlin installation.

Merlin 65 No.721

Contract: Engs 2073   First flight after conversion 7 February 1943
Installation and handling trials (3.15)

Despatched 25 February 1943 to AFDU Duxford.

Returned to Hucknall 3 May 1943 from 8th Fighter Command, USAAF Bovingdon.

Despatched 11 May 1943 to Rotol's, Staverton.

Returned to Hucknall 17 June 1943. Extended leading edge fin fitted.

Merlin 65 No.82459   Installation flight (0.20)

Despatched 26 June 1943 to 8th Fighter Command, USAAF Bovingdon.

AM148

Arrived 6 June 1943 from 51MU Lichfield.

Allison V1710 F3R No.6643

Contract: SB27058   Dismantled to provide parts for rear-engined
Flying Test Bed. Project cancelled.

Struck off Rolls-Royce charge 4 May 1944.

AM203

Arrived 9 August 1942 from Lockheed Aircraft Corporation, Abbotsinch.

Allison V1710 F3R No.6779

Contract: B.118479/40   Conversion to Merlin installation.

Merlin 65 No.82509
Contract Engs 2073   First flight after conversion 13 December 1942
                      Installation and handling trials (2.50)
                      Level speed performance calibration (10.20)
                      Delivery flights (2.40)
Despatched 16 December 1942 to A&AEE Boscombe Down.
Returned to Hucknall 21 December 1942.
Despatched 23 December 1942 to AFDU Duxford.
Returned to Hucknall 15 January 1943.
Despatched 26 January 1942 to AFDU Duxford.
Returned to Hucknall 22 March 1943 from 8th Fighter Command, USAAF
Bovingdon. Extended leading edge fin fitted.
Despatched 5 May 1943 to AFDU Wittering.
Returned to Hucknall 27 October 1943. No further flying.
Despatched 24 January 1944 to 20 MU Aston Down.

AM208
Arrived 3 August 1942 from Lockheed Aircraft Corporation, Abbotsinch.
Allison V1710 F3R No.9020
Contract: B.118479/40   Conversion to Merlin Installation.
Merlin 65 No.81953
Contract Engs 2073   First flight after conversion 13 November 1942
                      Installation and handling trials (3.15)
Despatched 28 November 1942 to A&AEE Boscombe Down.
Returned to Hucknall 24 December 1942.
Merlin 65 No.82445   Installation and despatch flight (1.35)
Despatched 12 February 1943 to A&AEE Boscombe Down.

AM245
Arrived 6 June 1943 from 51MU Lichfield.
Allison V1710 F3R No.9073
Contract: SB27058   Dismantled to provide parts for rear-engined
                     Flying Test Bed. Project cancelled.
Struck off Rolls-Royce charge 4 May 1944.

FB356
Arrived 23 June 1944 from 3501 SU Cranfield.
Packard Merlin V1650-7 No.V320453
Contract: Engs 2832   Performance investigation at +25 lb boost (0.45)
                       Delivery flight to 3501 SU (0.20)
Despatched 27 June 1944 to 3501 SU Coltishall.

FX852
Arrived 11 November 1943 from Lockheed Aircraft Corporation, Speke.

Packard Merlin V1650-3 No.B95

Contract: Engs 2832   Engine breather loss investigation (11.15)
                         Spark plug investigation (52.30)
                         Installation check flight (2.00)

Force landed 19 July 1944 at Weston on Trent, Derbyshire.

Disposed of by 58MU Newark.

FX858

Arrived 19 October 1943 from Lockheed Aircraft Corporation, Speke.

Packard Merlin V1650-3 No.B65

Contract: Engs 2832   Fuel consumption tests (4.10)
                         Engine breather loss investigation (16.35)
                         General investigation into operating at
                         + 15 lb boost (7.45)

Merlin RM.14.SM
Special No.90353   Performance investigation on Merlin 100
                         series type engine (16.05)
                         Spark plug investigation into operating
                         at + 25 lb boost (1.15)
                         Heat transfer investigation (5.00)
                         Endurance flying on Merlin 100 (6.35)
                         Endurance flying with SU fuel injection pump (3.10)

Despatched 31 March 1944 to A&AEE Boscombe Down.
Returned to Hucknall 28 April 1944.
Despatched 4 May 1944 to AFDU Wittering.
Returned to Hucknall 8 May 1944.
Despatched 9 May 1944 to AFDU Wittering.
Returned to Hucknall 30 May 1944.

Merlin RM.17.SM
No.90369   Installation and handling trials (0.45)

Force landed 19 September 1944 at RAF Syerston (reduction gear failure).

Merlin RM.14.SM
Special No.90353   Performance calibration (6.15)

Merlin RM.17.SM
No.90369   Installation and handling trials (5.30)
                         Performance calibration (3.10)

Force landed 1 May 1945 at RAF Bottesford, (con-rod failure).

Despatched 15 June 1945, by road, by 58MU Newark to Air Service Training, Kidlington.

FX901

Arrived 13 October 1943 from Lockheed Aircraft Corporation, Speke

Packard Merlin V1650-3 No.B263
Contract: Engs 2832   Engine breather loss investigation (5.30)
                        Carburettor investigation (3.00)
Packard Merlin
V1650-3 No. B95   Engine breather loss investigation (23.50)
                        Oil system investigation (anti frothing
                        additives) (4.00)
                        Spark plug investigation (effect of high
                        charge temperatures) (38.05)
                        Heat transfer investigation (4.00)
Merlin 113 No.90351 Performance investigation at +25 lb boost
                        and endurance flying (16.05)
                        Reliability flying (6.05)
Despatched 8 June 1945 to 30MU Llandow.

FX935
Arrived 10 July 1944 from 3501 SU Cranfield.
Packard Merlin V1650-7 No.V320135
Contract: Engs 2832   General flight investigation and clearance
                        for running at +25 lb boost (1.20)
Packard Merlin
V1650-7 No.V322306   Continuation of tests (2.25)
Despatched 24 July 1944 to 3501 SU Cranfield.

FX945
Arrived 10 July 1944 from 3501 SU Cranfield.
Packard Merlin V1650-7 No.V320197
Contract: Engs 2832   General flight investigation and clearance
                        for running at +25 lb boost (3.50)
Despatched 18 July 1944 to 3501 SU Cranfield.

FX984
Arrived first week in January 1944.
                        Fitment of new exhaust manifolds.
Nothing else known.

FZ185
Arrived 21 January 1944 from Lockheed Aircraft Corporation, Renfrew
Packard Merlin V1650-3 No.V300856
Contract: Engs 2832   Check flight re engine breather loss (0.25)
Despatched 28 March 1944 to 20MU Aston Down.

HB890

Arrived 17 August 1944 from R.Malcolm Ltd. White Waltham.
Packard Merlin V1650-7 No.V320971
Packard Merlin V1650-7 No.V321315
Contract: Engs 2832   Evaluation of Rolls-Royce governor-
controlled fuel injection pump operating
at +25 lb boost (3.45)

Packard Merlin
V1650-7 No.V320789   Continuation of tests (1.25)
Contract: Engs 4086   Continuation of tests prior to engine
being sent to USA (5.40)

Packard Merlin
V1650-3 No.V300766   Evaluation of Rolls-Royce governor-
controlled fuel injection pump (14.15)
Despatched 9 June 1945 to 20MU Aston Down.

43-6557

Arrived 12 June 1944 from USAAF Station 470, Hitcham (Wattisham).
Packard Merlin V1650-3 No.V300823
Contract: Engs 2832   Fitment of Spitfire type header tank and
flame damping exhaust manifolds.
Delivery flight to Coningsby (0.20)
Despatched 30 June 1944 to RAF Coningsby.

43-12425

Arrived 7 October 1943 from USAAF Station 112, Bovingdon.
Packard Merlin V1650-3 No.B264
Contract: Engs 2832   Engine breather loss investigation (3.10)
Despatched 21 October 1943 to USAAF Station 112, Bovingdon.

44-14244

Arrived 31 August 1944 from USAAF Station 112, Bovingdon.
Packard Merlin V1650-7 No.V323513
Contract: Engs 4086   Installation of airscrew and throttle
interconnected controls.
No development or check flights carried out.
Despatched 17 January 1945 to USAAF Station 112, Bovingdon.

N1202

Arrived 21 May 1951.
Packard Merlin V1650-9
Maintenance checks prior to returning to
the USA via the North Pole.
Despatched 23 May 1951 to London Airport.

The engines

All Allison engines referred to in the story are of the V1710-39 (F3R) type and none of the aircraft received at Hucknall had the improved V1710-81 variant installed. They had a single supercharger stage with a single drive gear ratio. Bore was 5 1/2 inches and stroke 6 inches. Compression ratio was 6.65:1, weight 1335 lb and displacement 28 litres (1710 cubic inches). Maximum rpm was 3000.

Certain basic details of the Merlin remained the same irrespective of mark number and manufacturer. These were:- Bore 5.4 inches, stroke 6 inches, compression ratio 6:1, displacement 27 litres (1649 cubic inches) and maximum rpm 3000. The weights of the two-stage engines varied slightly between 1640 and 1670 lb. according to which accessories were fitted.

When major internal differences affecting the operation occurred a new rating number was given. Typical examples were a change in supercharger gear ratio, and two-stage instead of single-stage supercharging. Change in the propellor reduction gear ratio or the coolant flow, for example, would alter the mark number but not the rating. By changing the Merlin 61 (RM.8.SM) supercharger gear ratios to provide more power at lower altitudes a new lineage was created - the Merlin 65 (RM.10.SM) developed especially for the Mustang project. A further change, this time to the reduction gear ratio to suit Spitfire operation, resulted in one of the finest of all Merlins - the Mark 66.

The Packard V1650-3 was neither one nor the other on account of its Americanisation but was the near equivalent to the Merlin 61, being best suited to the high altitude role. With the realisation that fighting in the European Theatre of Operations usually took place at altitudes of up to 20,000 feet, the supercharger gear ratios were lowered accordingly to give the V1650-7 variant which was rated at RM.10.SM, there being no major differences between it and the Merlin 65/66 series.

The Griffon plays only a minor role in the story but for completeness its details are included. Bore 6 inches, stroke 6.6 inches, compression ratio 6:1, weight 1980 lb (2-stage engines), displacement 36.7 litres (2239 cubic inches). Whereas most Merlin marks employed electric starting, the Griffon invariably had a Coffman cartridge starter.

The following list of engines referred to in the story gives all the important features of each type. The Merlin 61, being the first of the two-stage fighter variants, is included for comparison. All powers shown are for engines operating on 100 octane fuel. These are static figures; when in the air the powers and Full Throttle Heights are higher due to the ram-air effect down the carburettor intake.

ENGINE	RATING	S/C ROTOR DIAMETER	S/C GEAR RATIO	R/GEAR RATIO	CARBURETTOR	MAX BOOST lb.	Hg.	COMBAT POWER RATINGS/REMARKS
Allison V1710–39	—	9.5	8.8	.50	Bendix	8	46	1150 BHP/12,000'
Merlin 28	RM.3.SM	10.25	8.15/9.49	.42	Bendix	16	63	1460 BHP/6250'/MS—1435 BHP/11,000'/FS Corresponds to V1650-1 (normally +9 boost)
Merlin 61	RM.8.SM	11.5/10.1	6.39/8.03	.42	SU Float	15	61	1560 BHP/12,000'/MS—1370 BHP/24,000'/FS Never flown in Mustang
Merlin 65	RM.10.SM	12.0/10.1	5.79/7.06	.42	Bendix	18	67	1705 BHP/5750'/MS—1580 BHP/16,000'/FS Development only
Merlin 66	RM.10.SM	12.0/10.1	5.79/7.06	.477	Bendix	18	67	1705 BHP/5750'/MS—1580 BHP/16,000'/FS Interconnected throttle/pitch control
Merlin 70/71	RM.11.SM	12.0/10.1	6.39/8.03	.477	Bendix	18	67	1655 BHP/10,000'/MS—1475 BHP/22,250'/FS Shunt cooling in Mustang X only
—	RM.14.SM	12.0/10.1	5.79/7.06	.42	SU Pump	25	81	2150 BHP/2000'/MS—1890 BHP/14,750'/FS First of Merlin 100 series
Merlin 113	RM.16.SM	12.0/10.1	6.39/8.03	.42	SU Pump	18	67	1690 BHP/13,000'/MS—1435 BHP/27,250'/FS Reversed coolant flow
Packard V1650–3	—	12.0/10.1	6.39/8.09	.479	Bendix	18	67	1600 BHP/12,000'/MS—1330 BHP/23,000'/FS First Packard two-stage Merlin
Packard V1650–7	RM.10.SM	12.0/10.1	5.80/7.34	.479	Bendix	18	67	1720 BHP/6200'/MS—1505 BHP/19,300'/FS Near equivalent to Merlin 66
—	RM.17.SM	12.7/10.7	5.79/7.06	.42	RR Pump	30	91	2200 BHP/2000'/MS—2100 BHP/15,000'/FS Ultimate fighter variant, No production
Griffon 61	RG.4.SM	13.4/11.3	5.84/7.58	.451	Bendix	18	67	2055 BHP/8250'/MS—1780 BHP/22,000'/FS Never flown in Mustang or FTB
Griffon 65	RG.4.SM	13.4/11.3	5.16/6.79	.51	Bendix	18	67	2120 BHP/1250'/MS—1935 BHP/15,500'/FS Never flown in Mustang or FTB

Merlin 66

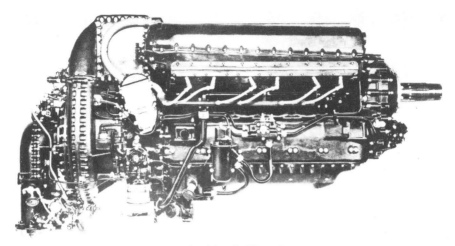

Packard Merlin V1650-3

THE MUSTANG P51B

" the longest-ranged single-engined fighter in the world."

The New York "Herald-Tribune," commenting on
the new Mustang, said : " Many have long regarded
it as the best fighter plane produced in the States,
but it remained for the British to discover it. If it
had not been for British orders, it would never
have been developed at all. Its full potentialities
were brought out only when the British designed
Rolls-Royce Merlin engine was installed."

ROLLS-ROYCE
MERLIN ENGINES

APPENDIX III

Mustang X AM.208
(Merlin 65)

Climb and level speed performance

Period of tests:- 5.12.42 - 2.4.43

1. Introduction

Climb and level speed performance has been measured on Mustang X AM.208. This aircraft was basically an NA-83 version, modified by Messrs. Rolls-Royce to take a Merlin 65, an intercooled, two-stage supercharged engine with a .42 reduction gear and a Stromberg carburettor.

A 4-bladed 10′9″ diameter propellor was fitted for these tests.

2. Condition of aircraft relevant to tests

2.1   General. The aircraft, together with the modifications entailed through fitting the Merlin 65 engine, has been described in the 1st Part of Report No.A.&.A.E.E./781,a. A brief description of the aircraft as tested is given below:-

2.11   Engine and cooling installation

A Merlin 65 engine housed in a modified cowling.
Engine air intake, intake for intercooler radiator duct and intercooler radiator, all housed in a common fairing beneath the engine.
Rectangular louvred exits for intercooler radiator air on either side of the engine cowling.
No air cleaners or ice guard over the engine air intake.
Individual ejector exhaust stubs.
A 10′9″ diameter, 4-bladed Rotor propellor, type R5/4F5/4.
Coolant radiator and oil cooler installed in the normal NA-83 under-fuselage duct.
Intake scoop to radiator duct sealed.

2.12   Armament & external fittings

4 x .30″ and 2 x .50″ guns in the wings with their ejection chutes open and leading edge ports sealed.
No fuselage guns fitted.
Bead sight in front of bullet proof windscreen.
Aerial mast behind pilot's hood with a W/T serial to the fin tip.
I.F.F. aerials from the tailplane tips to the sides of the fuselage.

2.2   Loading. The tests were made at a take-off weight of 9,100 lb.

118

2.3   Engine numbers and limitations. Two Merlin 65 engines were used for these tests. The first engine, Nos.81953/A331468, failed during the tests and was replaced by another Merlin 65, Nos.82445/A331715.

The operational limitations of the above engines applicable to the tests made are given below:-

	R.P.M.	Boost (lb/sq.in)
Maximum for all-out level flight and combat (5 min. limit)	3000	+18
Maximum for climb at normal rating (1 hr. limit)	2850	+12

3.   Tests made

As mentioned in para 2.3., the first engine fitted in this aircraft failed during the course of the tests and they were completed with a second engine which was installed by Messrs. Rolls-Royce Ltd. Preliminary results obtained with the second engine made it clear that the speed performance of the aircraft was worse with this engine, and accordingly the performance is given for both engines.

Details of the tests made are:-

3.1   With the first engine fitted.

(a)   Partial climbs at combat rating to determine the best climbing speed.
(b)   One climb at combat rating using M.S. supercharger gear only, and two using F.S. supercharger gear only to determine the optimum height to change supercharger gear.

The radiator exit duct was fully open for the above tests. The engine failed before any full climbs could be carried out.

(c)   Measurements of maximum level speeds with radiator exit duct flap closed in M.S. and F.S. supercharger gears. Heights from 2,000 to 32,000 ft. were covered by these measurements.

3.2   With the second engine fitted.

(a)   Several full climbs at combat rating using the climbing speed obtained with the first engine fitted and changing supercharger gear at the optimum height also obtained with the first engine. All except one of these climbs were terminated at 35,000 ft. owing to fuel pressure failure and resultant engine cutting. This was cured by fitting an S.P.E. booster pump, and a climb was made to 38,000 ft. to determine the performance near the aircraft's ceiling.
(b)   Two climbs at normal rating (S.P.E. pump fitted) using the same climbing speed as that for combat rating. As explained in the 1st Part of this Report, this speed was used for cooling purposes. A brief partial climb test was made at normal rating indicating a best climbing speed slightly lower than that used, but it also indicated that the climbing speed was not critical from the point of view of performance.

The radiator exit duct flap was fully open during all the climbs.

(c) Measurements of maximum level speeds with the radiator exit duct flap closed, in M.S. and F.S. supercharger gears. Heights from 2,000 to 33,000 ft. were covered by these measurements.

(d) The position error of the pressure head installation was measured over the aircraft's speed range in level flight, flaps and undercarriage up, by the aneroid method.

4. Results of tests

The performance results have been corrected to standard atmospheric conditions and the level speeds to 85% of the take-off weight, viz. 8,650 lb. by the methods given in Report No. A.& A.E.E./Res/170. The compressibility corrections in the level speed results have been calculated using the methods of the Addendum to Report No. A.& A.E.E./Res/147. A strut correction has also been applied to the indicated airspeeds in the level speed results. The source of this correction is A.R.C. Report 6420. Insufficient evidence was obtained of the climb performance at combat rating with the first engine fitted to enable two sets of climb results to be given. Hence only that measured with the second engine is given.

The full results of the tests made are to be found in the Tables and Figures at the end of the report. A summary of the performance results is given below:-

(i) Climb at combat rating. (2nd engine, radiator flap open).

Best climbing speed	= 195 m.p.h. A.S.I. to 19,000 ft.
	decreasing speed by 7 m.p.h. per 2,000 ft. thereafter.
Rate of climb at F.T.H, M.S. gear	= 3560 ft/min at 7,500 ft.
Rate of climb at F.T.H, F.S. gear	= 2840 ft/min at 18,000 ft.
Time to reach 10,000 ft	= 2.9 mins.
Time to reach 20,000 ft	= 6.3 mins.
Time to reach 30,000 ft	= 11.3 mins.
Estimated Service Ceiling	= 38,500 ft.
Estimated absolute ceiling	= 39,000 ft.
Optimum height to change supercharger gear	= 15,000 ft.

(ii) Climb at normal rating. (2nd engine, radiator flap open).

climbing speed used	= Same as for climb at combat rating (i)
Rate of climb at F.T.H, M.S. gear	= 2600 ft/min at 11,300 ft.
Rate of climb at F.T.H, F.S. gear	= 2110 ft/min at 22,000 ft.
Time to reach 10,000 ft	= 3.9 mins.
Time to reach 20,000 ft	= 8.3 mins.
Time to reach 30,000 ft	= 14.3 mins.
Estimated Service Ceiling	= 37,700 ft.
Estimated absolute ceiling	= 38,200 ft.
Optimum height to change supercharger gear	= 15,000 ft.

(iii) All-out level speeds. (Radiator flap closed)

	1st engine	2nd engine
Max true airspeed, 2,000 ft/M.S. gear	= 360 m.p.h.	356 m.p.h
Max true airspeed, F.T.H./M.S. gear	= 406/10,800 ft	395/ 9,800 ft
Max true airspeed, F.T.H./F.S. gear	= 433/22,000 ft	425/21,400 ft
Optimum height to change supercharger gear	= 15,500 ft	= 14,000 ft

Mustang X AM 208
Performance on climb

——— At combat rating
— — — At normal rating
Radiator exit duct flap open
Take-off weight - 9100 lb

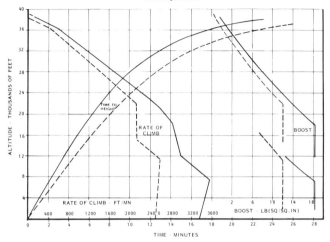

PERFORMANCE ON CLIMB AT COMBAT RATING - 3000 RPM
Take off weight - 9100 lb   Radiator flap fully open

Merlin 65 No.81953

HEIGHT Feet	TIME min/sec	RATE OF CLIMB Ft/min	T.A.S. m.p.h.	A.S.I. m.p.h	CORRECTIONS m.p.h P.E. C.E.		BOOST lb/sq.in.	S/C GEAR
0	0						18.2	MS
2000	0.36	3420	199	195	-1.7	-0.1	18.2	"
4000	1.09	3470	205	195	-1.7	-0.2	18.2	"
6000	1.45	3520	211	195	-1.7	-0.3	18.2	"
*7500	2.09	3560	216	195	-1.7	-0.5	18.2	"
10000	2.54	3250	224	195	-1.7	-0.7	14.8	"
12000	3.33	3000	231	195	-1.7	-0.9	12.5	"
							18.2	FS
14000	4.12	2950	238.5	195	-1.7	-1.1	18.2	"
16000	4.54	2900	246	195	-1.7	-1.3	18.2	"
*18000	5.36	2840	254	195	-1.7	-1.5	18.2	"
20000	6.18	2680	258.5	192	-1.5	-1.7	16.1	"
22000	7.06	2480	258.5	185	-0.9	-1.8	14.0	"
24000	7.57	2220	257	178	-0.4	-1.8	11.9	"
26000	8.54	1960	257	171	0	-1.9	9.9	"
28000	10.00	1700	256	164	+0.6	-1.9	7.9	"
30000	11.18	1420	255.5	157	+1.1	-1.9	6.0	"
32000	12.51	1140	254	150	+1.6	-1.9	4.3	"
34000	14.51	860	253	143	+2.2	-2.0	2.8	"
35000	16.06	730	253	140	+2.5	-2.0	2.0	"
36000	17.36	600	250.5	136	+2.8	-1.9	1.3	"
37000	19.39	400	252	133	+3.0	-1.9	0.6	"
38000	23.03	200	250.5	129	+3.4	-1.9	0.2	"

*Full throttle heights   Supercharger gear change at 12,000 ft.

Estimated Service ceiling = 38,500 ft.
Estimated absolute ceiling= 39,000 ft.

Mustang X AM 208
Level speeds and boosts at heights
Corrected to 95% of the T.O. weight viz 8640 lb

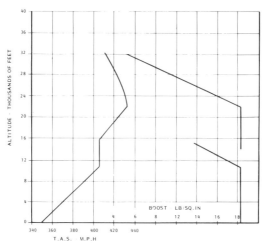

LEVEL SPEED PERFORMANCE - 3000 RPM

Corrected to 95% of take-off weight - 8650 lb

Merlin 65 No. 81953

HEIGHT Feet	T.A.S. m.p.h	A.S.I. m.p.h.	CORRECTIONS m.p.h. P.E.	C.E	STRUT	BOOST 1b/Sq.in	S/C GEAR
2000	360	363.5	-14.5	+0.5	+0.1	18.2	MS
4000	370.5	364	-14.5	-0.4	+0.2	18.2	"
6000	381	364.5	-14.6	-1.4	+0.3	18.2	"
8000	391.5	363	-14.5	-2.4	+0.4	18.2	"
* 10800	406	362	-14.4	-3.9	+0.6	18.2	"
12000	405.5	355	-13.8	-4.3	+0.7	17.0	"
14000	405	343.5	-13.0	-5.1	+0.7	14.8	"
15500	404.5	335.5	-12.4	-5.6	+0.8	13.6	"
						18.2	FS
16000	407	335.5	-12.4	-6.0	+0.8	18.2	"
18000	416	332	-12.1	-7.0	+1.1	18.2	"
20000	424.5	328.5	-11.8	-8.1	+1.4	18.2	"
* 22000	433	325	-11.5	-9.2	+1.8	18.2	"
24000	430.5	312	-10.6	-9.5	+1.8	16.0	"
26000	427	298.5	- 9.6	-9.8	+1.7	13.7	"
28000	423	285	- 8.6	-10.0	+1.6	11.4	"
30000	417.5	271	- 7.5	-10.1	+1.5	9.2	"
32000	411.5	257.5	- 6.5	-10.1	+1.4	6.9	"

* Full throttle heights   Supercharger gear change at 15,500 ft.

5. Discussion of results

It will be seen from the level speed results that there is an appreciable difference in the performance of the aircraft with the two engines fitted. No changes likely to affect the level speed performance were made between the two sets of tests with the exception of the change of engine. The difference in speed performance, therefore, must be accounted for by differences in the powers of the engines and any small differences in the installation (such as a badly fitted or deformed air intake).

The greatest aeroplane in the world, according to the Americans, was the Mustang. It was engined by the Rolls-Royce Company and ordered into production by the Prime Minister of Great Britain.

Lord Beaverbrook

ROLLS-ROYCE
MERLIN ENGINES

APPENDIX IV

AIR FIGHTING DEVELOPMENT UNIT

R.A.F. STATION DUXFORD

INTERIM REPORT No.64

on

COMPARATIVE TRIALS OF NEW LOW ALTITUDE FIGHTERS
SPITFIRE IX (MERLIN 66) AND MUSTANG X (MERLIN 65)

INTRODUCTION

1. In accordance with instructions from Air Ministry (D.A.T.), C.S.1800 dated 30th September 1942, tactical trials have now been carried out with the Mustang X. Aircraft No. AM.203 was delivered to this unit on 23.12.42 and this aircraft has been compared with Spitfire IX No.BS.552 fitted with a similar engine which was available throughout the trial. A second Spitfire IX with this type of engine, No.BS.543, had also been flown at this unit. Further flying is to be done by pilots from the U.S.A.A.F., on the Mustang X, when it will be compared with modern American fighters, but the arrangements of the U.S.A.F made it impossible for these pilots to be made available during the early part of the trials and a report will therefore be rendered at the completion of their flying.

DESCRIPTION

General

2. Both aircraft were fitted with same the type of Merlin engine which is known as the Merlin 65 when fitted to the Mustang, and the 66 when installed in the Spitfire. Both are developments of the Merlin 61, and are specially designed for high performance at low altitude. The engines differ only in that the Mustang has a propellor reduction gear of .42, while that of the Spitfire is .477. A Bendix carburettor which prevents cutting under negative 'G' is fitted in both cases and the full throttle boost allowable for combat has been increased to +18 lb. The supercharger gear ratios are 5.79 and 7.06, but Spitfire BS.552 was in fact fitted with an earlier type engine having an M.S. gear of 5.52, giving a full throttle height of 7,000 feet. The slightly higher M.S. gear of 5.79 increases the full throttle height to 11,000 feet and will be the standard gear provided in production. Spitfire IX No.BS.543 was flown for a short time at this Unit having this higher M.S. supercharger gear.

Spitfire IX.

3. The alterations made to this aircraft affect the engine and its installation only and it is otherwise a standard Spitfire IX (see A.F.D.U.Reports Nos. 46 and 57). The earlier aircraft, including BS.543, had Dural propellors and their

all-up weight down to about 7,260 lb. The fitting of the Bendix carburettor has been incorporated with an immersed fuel pump which this Unit was instructed to use for starting up, take-off and aerobatics.

It was found, however, that the pump was unnecessary for starting, take-off or any flying manoeuvres, except possibly to restart the engine after a dead cut due to inverted flying with almost empty tanks.

The pump was not used after the first week's flying and has never been needed, although unsuccessful attempts were made to make the engine cut with only a little fuel in the tanks. The pressurised fuel system is adequate for the needs of the engine at altitude. No fuel inter-coolers are fitted and they do not appear necessary. These is no mixture control in the cockpit and no gate on the throttle. Otherwise, no alterations have been made to the aircraft and its appearance is identical with other Spitfire IX's, which is a strong point tactically as the enemy will never know which type of Spitfire he is fighting. Full throttle heights are 11,000 and 22,000 feet. The superchargers are changed automatically at 12,500 feet on the climb.

Mustang X

4.   With completely redesigned nose cowlings the Merlin 65 has fitted very neatly into the Mustang. This engine runs more smoothly than any other that has been flown at this Unit previously as it is mounted on large rubber blocks. The radiator has been retained in the original position as for the Allison motor and the air intake has been placed underneath the engine along with the inter-cooler radiator instead of on top as with the Allison, in order to improve the pilot's view. The front scoop of the radiator has been sealed in the fully closed position so that only the rear flap moves. The operation of the radiator flap is automatic, being controlled hydraulically on the earlier models and by compressed air on later aircraft through a thermostat control. Immersed pumps are fitted to both fuel tanks and are required for all flying above 18,000 feet. No pressurising of the tanks appears necessary and both tanks have had their capacity increased to 75 gallons, thus giving a total capacity of 150 gallons. The full throttle heights for this engine in the Mustang are about 11,000 and 22,000 feet. The automatic supercharger change operates at 12,500 feet on the climb. The aircraft available at this Unit had an Hydulignum propellor of 11' 4" diameter, but it is known that trials are being conducted elsewhere with the standard Spitfire propellor of 10' 9".

5.   The Model 83 Mustang was used for the Merlin installation as a test bench and so the armament consists only of the 2 x .50 and 4 x .30 calibre guns in the wings, there being no room for the installation of .50 guns in the fuselage. It is thought that the 4-cannon wing which is now available on the Model 91 Mustang will provide a quite satisfactory armament if this engine installation is to go into production.

The aircraft flown in this Unit weighed 9,065 lb, and is thus about 1,800 lb heavier than the Spitfire; with the cannon wing it would weigh 9,200 lb. Ballast weighing 70 lb was carried in the tail. The aircraft also had a special high polish finish which is particularly easy to keep free from oil and grit, but is thought that owing to the already clean design of the airframe this special finish has not added noticeably to the aircraft's performance.

6.   The flying trials on this aircraft were delayed partly for the fitting of locks to the leading edge of the wheel fairings which were tending to blow open at high speeds, and also for the removal of the engine which became necessary owing to the destruction of a washer between the supercharger casing and the crankcase.

TACTICAL

Flying Characteristics

7.   (i) Spitfire IX.   There is very little difference in the general characteristics of this Spitfire from other Spitfire IXs. It was, however, found that the aileron control was considerably worse than is usual on the IX and a considerable amount of flying had to be carried out with alterations of rigging and various pairs of ailerons in order to get lateral control that was acceptable, but even with the best pair of ailerons at the Unit's disposal the control was not as good as a standard Spitfire VB. The earlier part of the trials was carried out with wing tips in position and a few flights were made at the end with the wing tips clipped. This improved the all-round fighting capabilities of the IX without detracting noticeably from the excellent rate of climb.

(ii) Mustang X.   The Mustang X is capable of very high speeds in level flight and dive, the aileron control being particularly good at the higher speeds. The elevators have become a trifle heavier than in the Allison engined version and the longitudinal stability has been increased making steady climbs and instrument flying easy. The rudder requires more trimming than previously with the increased torque from the engine and accurate turns, especially to the right, are difficult to carry out. In particular, changes in engine setting during a turn at once produced a noticeable wander. These are serious disadvantages in a fighter, as no matter how good a marksman the pilot is he will not be able to shoot accurately in a turn which has an element of skid or slip in it. These inaccurate turns were also very noticeable at altitude as they caused temporary misting up of the cockpit on the side towards which the aircraft skidded. Steps are, however, in hand to increase the fin area and improve the rudder control which is at present considered inadequate. Take-off is straightforward with little tendency to swing and the approach and landing easy at an I.A.S. of 110 m.p.h.

Performance

8.   The Spitfire IX being the lighter aircraft has a slightly better acceleration from cruising flight to its maximum speeds. The Mustang varies between 12 and 22 m.p.h. faster than the Spitfire up to about 34,000 feet, at which height the Spitfire becomes the faster. Maxima for the Spitfire and Mustang as given by the A.& A.E.E., are as follows:-

126

	Spitfire	Mustang
11,000 feet in M.S. gear	384 m.p.h.	404 m.p.h.
22,000 feet in F.S. gear	407 m.p.h.	430 m.p.h.

Climb

9. The Spitfire climbs about 800 ft/min faster than the Mustang up to 20,000 feet, after which its superiority drops off slightly. The rates of climb as obtained by the A.& A.E.E. were for a Spitfire fitted with a dural propellor and other fittings likely to be removed in operations, which made it about 200 lb heavier than the aircraft will probably be in Service, so that better results still can be expected. In the case of the Mustang the figures given are for an aircraft with the smaller propellor, so that a better climb can be anticipated with the larger one as flown in this Unit. The operational ceiling of 1,000 ft/min is reached at 37,500 feet in 13 minutes in the Spitfire and at 34,000 feet in 13 3/4 minutes in the Mustang. The angle of climb for both aircraft is very steep; in the Spitfire it is particularly difficult for the pilot to see the horizon in the initial parts of the climb owing to the high angle of the nose. The Mustang climbs at a higher speed (195 m.p.h. I.A.S. to 19,000 feet) and is much more stable than the Spitfire, it being possible to trim with hands and feet off. Zoom climbs were carried out to compare the two aircraft in which it was found that from fast cruising conditions the Spitfire was faster from ground level to 10,000 feet by 15 seconds; from 10,000 to 20,000 feet by 17 seconds; and from 20,000 to 30,000 feet by 40 seconds.

Dive

10. The Mustang out-dives the Spitfire very easily, being especially quick to accelerate away at full throttle. In the dive the rudder requires a considerable amount of left trim, but the elevator control is good, there being no tendency to recover fiercely and the amount of trim required from cruising flight is only very little. At the end of a dive the Mustang retains its speed very much longer than the Spitfire.

Manoeuvrability

11. The aircraft were compared at varying heights for their powers of manoeuvrability and it was found throughout that the Mustang, as was expected, did not have so good a turning circle as the Spitfire. By the time they were at 30,000 feet the Mustang's controls were found to be rather mushy, while the Spitfire's were still very crisp and even in turns during which 15° of flap were used on the Mustang, the Spitfire had no difficulty in out-turning it. In rate of roll, however, it found that while the Spitfire is superior in rolling quickly from one turn to another at speeds up to 300 m.p.h., there is very little to choose between the two at 350 m.p.h., I.A.S. and at 400 m.p.h. the Mustang is definitely superior, its controls remaining far lighter at high speeds than those of the Spitfire. When the Spitfire was flown with its wings clipped, the rate of roll was improved at 400 m.p.h., so as to be almost identical with the Mustang. The manoeuvrability of the Mustang, however, is severely limited by the lack of directional stability which necessitates very heavy forces on the rudder to keep the aircraft steady. The trim requires re-setting for almost every alteration

of engine setting or increase or decrease of speed. If trimmed for the climb and then suddenly rolled over into a dive, it is difficult to hold the Mustang in the required line of flight and shooting at or even following the curve of another aircraft in a dive is not easy unless the aircraft is retrimmed as it gathers speed.

Sighting View

12.   The replacing of the air intake below the engine on the Merlin 65 installation of the Mustang has improved the pilot's sighting view to 120 m.p.h. The Spitfire's sighting view has not been altered from an equivalent 100 m.p.h.

Low Flying

13.   Although the view forwards and downwards from the Mustang is better than from the Spitfire, low flying is extremely uncomfortable with the present difficulty of executing accurate turns. As a result, any flying except straight and level makes the pilot feel that he lacks sufficient control to fly with sufficient precision to evade ground defences or natural obstacles. The Spitfire handles as well as previous Marks, except that the aileron control in BS.552 being stiffer than on the average Mark V, it required to be "flown" near the ground as it has lost some lateral stability and a dropped wing did not recover automatically.

Night Flying

14.   No night flying was carried out as both aircraft were fitted with open exhaust stubs.

OTHER POINTS

Mustang Pilot's Cockpit

15.   For a tall pilot the Mustang's cockpit is cramped so that he never gets a change to sit up straight as in the Spitfire, and even an average pilot with parachute and dinghy has to keep leaning forward to clear the roof. The view for search compares unfavourably with that from the balloon hood fitted to the Spitfire; in the Mustang the horizontal frames of the hood are level with the eye and are very wide, and the frames of the bullet-proof windscreen cause a fairly serious obstruction.

Mustang Heating

16.   The Mustang, now capable of good performance at higher altitude than was possible with the Allison engine, is considered to have inadequate cabin heating for work during Winter months. While there is a good flow of warm air through the warm duct, it is impossible for the pilot to close the cold duct completely.

Mustang Maintenance

17.   The only trouble encountered during the flight trials was that the wheel fairings were inclined to blow open at high speed. Front locks were fitted by the North American Company and a further modification was added by this

Unit in order to prevent hanging up which might happen if the cable used for the emergency gear should break. The modification consisted of stiffening Nos.1 & 2 formers and fitting with dural shear pins on to the front locks.

18. As mentioned above, the special finish on AM.203 is very easy to keep compared with the standard camouflage, and the adhesion to the skin of the airframe is better than that of British dope.

19. The Mustang has a more robust undercarriage and much wider track which can be used on rough ground with far greater safety than the Spitfire's.

CONCLUSIONS

20. The development of the Merlin 61 into the Merlin 65 and 66 and fitted in the Spitfire IX and Mustang X has made available two high performance low-altitude fighters that can be compared as follows:-

(i)   In level speed the Mustang is 12-22 m.p.h. faster than the Spitfire up to 30,000 feet.

(ii)   In rate of climb the Spitfire is better than the Mustang by about 800 ft/min up to 20,000 feet, the operational ceiling of 1,000 ft/min being 37,000 feet for the Spitfire and 34,000 for the Mustang.

(iii)   In the dive the Mustang is able to out-pace the Spitfire without difficulty.

(iv)   In turning and rolling manoeuvres the Spitfire is better, save that at 400 m.p.h., I.A.S., with standard wing it was a little inferior to the Mustang in rate of roll. With the Spitfire wing tips clipped their roll is identical at this speed. At altitude the Mustang's aileron control does not appear sufficient.

(v)   The Mustang suffers badly from lack of directional stability and adequate rudder control, both of which detract seriously from its fighting capabilities. Modifications are in hand to improve these qualities.

(vi)   The view for fighting and search generally from the Mustang is inferior to that from the Spitfire.

(vii)   The Mustang carries 150 gallons as compared with the Spitfire's 85 gallons. The latter can be increased by 30 gallons in a jettison tank.

D O Finlay[51]

AFDU/3/20/35
9th February 1943

Wing Commander
Commanding, A.F.D.U.

---

[51] The renowned athlete who, when a Pilot Officer in 1936, was selected as Captain of the British team at the Berlin Olympic games.

COMPARATIVE LEVEL SPEEDS
A & A.E.E. DATA

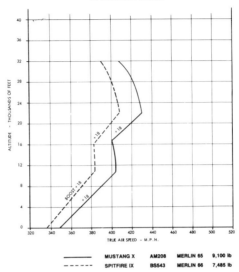

——— MUSTANG X	AM208	MERLIN 65	9,100 lb
- - - - SPITFIRE IX	BS543	MERLIN 66	7,485 lb

COMPARATIVE RATES OF CLIMB & TIME TO HEIGHT
A & A.E.E. DATA

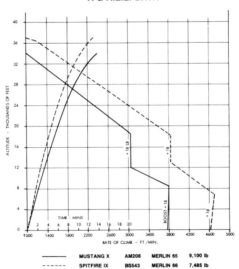

——— MUSTANG X	AM208	MERLIN 65	9,100 lb
- - - - SPITFIRE IX	BS543	MERLIN 66	7,485 lb

130

The performance of AM208 at Boscombe Down was compared with that of a specially modified Spitfire IX, BS543, both of which were powered by the low-altitude Merlin. The superiority in speed of the Mustang over the Spitfire is evident in spite of the latter's 1700 lb weight advantage - when it came to rate of climb the Spitfire was a clear winner because of it. The time curves show that the Spitfire IX took six minutes to reach 24,000 feet whereas the Mustang X took seven and a half. Spitfire BS543 was well chosen for the comparison for it played an important part in the Mustang X story. Along with BS354 and BS552 it was experimentally fitted with an RM.9.SM engine, which was the first low-altitude version of the Merlin 61. Tests with this combination proved successful but it was decided that the MS ratio should be increased from 5.52:1 to 5.79:1. Thus was born the RM.10.SM, to become the Merlin 65 and 66. In an assessment of Spitfire performances, Rolls-Royce stated that for the high and low-altitude types to be tactically successful, the aircraft should have the same exterior appearance and should be produced at the ratio of two low-altitude aircraft to every one high-altitude type.

THE MUSTANG . . . .

"*the longest-ranged single-engined fighter in the world.*"

The New York "Herald Tribune," commenting on the new Mustang, said: "Many have long regarded it as the best fighter plane produced in the States, but it remained for the British to discover it. If it had not been for British orders, it would never have been developed at all. Its full potentialities were brought out only when the British designed Rolls-Royce Merlin engine was installed.

ROLLS-ROYCE
MERLIN ENGINES

Allison versus Merlin

The Allison V1710 engine was unique in being America's only liquid-cooled engine to see front-line service in the Second World War. Just 61 cubic inches bigger in capacity than the Merlin its development had commenced in 1930, three years before the Merlin (PV-12). Such was Allison's lack of funds, resources and manpower that in the seven years it took to pass its 1000 hp typetest only about a dozen engines had been built, each one different from the last so that following a failure everything stopped until the engine was rebuilt.

Rolls-Royce, on the other hand, had built a couple of dozen Merlins by the time its 1000 hp typetest was passed late in 1936. The availability of an autonomous flight testing establishment at Hucknall meant that they had a Merlin flying just two years from commencement of design. In the case of the Allison the waiting time was six years.

To be fair, the procrastination was mainly a result of American government policy which did not support the military side of aero-engine development to the degree that the British government had done for its aero-engine industry. Consequently, the V1710 never achieved the dramatic increases in power and reliability brought about by a determined development programme as had the Merlin. It has to be remembered also, that by the time that America entered the war the Merlin had been in service for five years, over two years of which had been in actual front-line combat, and the lessons learned from the experience of the Battle of Britain and the night-bombing campaign were immeasurable.

There were other reasons for the Allison's slow performance on development and not just those of a mechanical nature. The U.S. Army, among other things, insisted on the production of three separate versions to suit the unorthodox designs of their future aircraft, two of which were shaft driven. There was also a bomber version consisting of two engines coupled side-by-side; the V3420.

The earlier models were turbocharged and it was not until 1938 that a conventional mechanical supercharger was married to the V1710 for installation in the Curtiss P-40. This was Allison's first excursion into mechanical supercharging, and a rush job at that, whereas Rolls-Royce had been developing theirs since the early Kestrel days dating back to 1927. At the time that Harker had proposed the Merlin for the Mustang the two companies were developing two-stage supercharged versions of their engines and once again it was the British company that had a clear technical superiority, despite the fact that both had run their prototype engines in the Spring of 1941. Within six months Rolls-Royce had their version in production as the Merlin 60 for the Wellington VI high-altitude bomber. Production of the fighter variant, the Merlin 61, had commenced in March 1942 for the Spitfire IX.

Rolls-Royce opted for the simplest of methods and placed the second rotor in tandem with the original which, as far as installation was concerned added just a few inches to the engine's overall length. Thus it was capable of occupying the space vacated by a single-stage model with the minimum of modification to the airframe. The second stage of the Allison blower, however, was a separate unit, hydraulically driven with a continuously variable speed in the same manner as the Daimler Benz DB601 in the Me109.

The reason for this lay in the method of production whereby all engines were built to a basic standard from whence a single-stage, two-stage or turbo supercharger was fitted accordingly for the aircraft for which it was intended. Mounting the second stage supercharger or turboblower remote from the engine itself meant that each installation was unique to a particular type of aircraft. The turbo method was particularly awkward as there had to be trunking to direct the exhaust to the turbine and more trunking to send the air to the engine.

To further increase the pressure ratio, and also the charge density, Rolls-Royce employed a device known as an intercooler (aftercooler in the U.S.) which reduced the temperature of the charge on leaving the supercharger, thus preventing the possibility of detonation. The Allison engine had no such device.

So, with Britain's decision that the Mustang should have a two-stage engine, the need for something to be done quickly, the technical superiority of the Merlin and the fact that there was no other suitable engine around, the choice was that of Hobson.

The Morris radiator with the oil cooler at its centre. Of the same dimensions as the original unit it had to cope with a 33% increase in heat dissipation. The curved water tubes are clearly seen.

133

APPENDIX VI

Throughout the text of this book there appear a number of technical terms, the use of which has been unavoidable. In order to prevent the use of overlong footnotes and because some readers may be unfamiliar with their meaning this Appendix will serve as a convenient vehicle to group them together and provide a means of enlightenment. The explanations given are aimed at layman level and as such shy from any professional dissertation.

Supercharger gearing

Moderate Supercharge (MS). The low gear of the supercharger which maintains the rated boost pressure up to a defined altitude known as the Full Throttle Height (FTH), after which the reduction in barometric pressure causes the boost to diminish.

Full Supercharge (FS). The high gear of the supercharger which takes over from MS to regain the rated boost and maintain it to the maximum FTH that has been selected for that particular mark of engine.

Full Throttle Height

The maximum altitude at which the rated boost pressure can be maintained at rated rpm. Above this height the boost pressure decreases and with it power and speed. The height is a condition of such factors as rpm, boost pressure, supercharger gear ratios, air intake efficiency etc.

Intercooling

Intercoolers (called aftercoolers in the USA) are usually fitted to highly-boosted engines equipped with a two stage supercharger; the Allison engine had a single-stage blower and so did not need one. Fuel vapour (charge) leaving the carburettor enters the first stage of the supercharger and is compressed, but to a safe level. It then continues on into the second stage where it is compressed yet again, in the case of the Merlin 61 to a maximum of $+18$ lb/sq in. above atmospheric pressure. Here the temperature rises to over 200° Centigrade, thus inviting the risk of detonation. It has, therefore, to be reduced to around 120°C. This is well below the figure required to suppress detonation but it has the further advantage in that the lowered charge temperature gives a mixture of increased density and thus greater power for a given boost pressure. Its position astride the supercharger precluded the possibility of feeding cooling air directly to it as the air-intake would create a drag problem and hinder the pilot's vision. To overcome this the intercooler is liquid-filled and this in turn cooled by a small separate radiator positioned somewhere convenient in the airstream.

The efficiency of charge cooling is defined as percentage intercooling. This is the ratio of the temperature drop through the intercooler matrix. A figure of 40% was considered satisfactory. In the two-stage supercharged Merlin the charge entered at around 200°C and was fed to the cylinders at about 120°C. The decrease in temperature produced the benefit of an increase in density.

Radiator suitability

Under certain conditions of flight, which took into account such factors as high ambient temperature (English Summer Maximum or Tropical) and flight regimes such as cruising, climb and all-out level speed (and, of course, taxying), along with the size of the radiator and its frontal area, a temperature was decided upon at which the coolant should leave the radiator. If a satisfactory temperature drop through the matrix was obtained, i.e., temperature out compared with temperature in, that permitted safe operation of the engine for a particular flight regime, then radiator suitability would be assessed as 100%. A correctly designed system would prevent overheating, particularly in the climb where air speed was at its lowest and engine RPM very high. Designing the optimum size of a radiator to suit all conditions was a precise art in order to prevent too large a frontal area for cruising or at high speed and too small for climbing. During the latter a variable flap at the exit would automatically control the velocity of the airflow through the duct to give the desired amount of cooling, albeit with a drag penalty.

Performance Testing

For level speed calibration the aircraft was flown at combat conditions (in the case of the Mustang X 3000 rpm + 18 lb boost) at low altitude along a set course for anything up to ten minutes, frequent readings being taken of all parameters until stable conditions were achieved after which the run was continued for another five minutes. A reciprocal course was then flown under similar conditions - this making sure that the aircraft flew through the same air mass. A number of such runs would be made until a set of figures were achieved that were in agreement. This exercise was then repeated in increasing altitudes of 2000 feet. As the Full Throttle Height was approached the levels were undertaken at 1000 feet increments so as to obtain a more accurate assessment of the FTH. The levels were continued beyond this level where, of course, the speeds gradually fell off with the diminishing boost pressure. When the FTH in MS gear was established the levels continued again in multiples of 2000 feet, but this time in FS gear. This went on until a set of plots had been obtained that covered the complete range of operating altitudes.

All this took a considerable amount of time and a series of flights would be undertaken before the whole envelope had been explored. The results, in the form of plots on a graph, were then analysed and a mean line drawn through the points to give a better visual presentation, the graph showing speed (horizontally) against altitude (vertically). As the Air Speed Indicator is operated by pressure in the pitot tube and because air pressure decreased with altitude the reading on the cockpit instrument is not accurate when compared with the actual speed of the aircraft. These speeds are known as "velocities" or Indicated Air Speed (IAS). The results were then corrected. A set of standard tables are referred to that give air densities at various altitudes and from these the corrections from IAS to True Air Speed (TAS) are made. Also taken into account are the air temperatures prevailing at the different altitudes, hence the reason for flying reciprocally through the same air mass. Another correction is made for Position Error. Air entering the pitot head is often influenced in some way or another by the aircraft's structure. All types of aircraft have a Position Error chart which gives the amount of speed you must add or subtract to obtain the accurate TAS under certain conditions of flight. So, having taken into account the air density and temperature, the Position Error (P.E.) and the Compressibility Error (C.E.) of the air in the pitot system, not forgetting instrument error, the exact speed of the aircraft is ascertained by applying the above correction factors to the Indicated Air Speed. True Air Speed must not be confused with Ground Speed which is aircraft speed relative to the ground.

When evaluating the climb performance the objective is to ascertain the best climbing speed at which the aircraft will maintain a constant climb at the specified engine rpm and boost pressure without exceeding the parameters set for coolant and oil temperatures. Normal climbs were undertaken at 2850 rpm and combat climbs at 3000 rpm, the two conditions producing different Full Throttle Heights.

Personalities

The following are brief biographies of some of those concerned with Rolls-Royce's involvement with the Mustang. The choice is restricted to those who, in the author's opinion, played a major role in the story, but is not meant in any way to detract any credit from those whose industriousness in their own fields of endeavour played an equally important part in the success of the project.

W O W Challier   R N Dorey

W O Witold Challier, seen here in later life, was born in Poland in 1904. He graduated in mechanical (aeronautical) engineering at the Technical University of Warsaw. At the outbreak of war he was Head of the Aircraft and Equipment Division of the Technical Institute for Aeronautics - the Polish equivalent of the RAE. Following the fall of Poland he, like so many of his countrymen, found his way to England and in January 1941 began his career with Rolls-Royce as their performance expert at Hucknall. How he came to Rolls-Royce is not known for certain but it is thought that he was directed there by the Polish exile organisation that was responsible for assessment of its technically talented countrymen and their deployment into areas that would be of benefit to the war effort. Challier himself became a member of the organisation.

In his almost thirty year career with the Company, all of which was devoted to performance, aerodynamic and project work, he earned himself a high reputation for his work, not only within the confines of Rolls-Royce but also within the industry itself - indeed, it is said that Sidney Camm of Hawker's was not averse to ringing him to seek his advice. He became Chief Project Engineer in 1949 and six years later transferred to Derby where he remained until his retirement in 1970.

Ray Dorey BSc FRAeS, was one of the most respected men in British aviation. A graduate of Bristol University, he joined Rolls-Royce in 1927 as an experimental tester and within two years he was working on the R engines for the 1929 Schnieder Trophy race and for Segrave's *Miss England* speed boat. In 1931 he was Assistant to the Chief Installation Engineer and put in charge of the development of the R engine for that year's Schnieder Trophy race, a task that was to squeeze around five years of development and testing into but a few months. The securing of the Trophy for all time and the achievement of an output of nearly 2800 bhp for an hour will forever stand as testament to his engineering capability. This statement in no way belittles the efforts of Hives, Lovesey, Ellor, Rubbra or Banks, each and every one of whom played a vital role in the venture but it was to Dorey that befell the task of team leadership during those crucial and all-to-few months prior to the race.

The following year he concentrated on installation problems and joined Jimmy Ellor, the supercharger expert, in this field visiting many aircraft companies both at home and abroad. This experience was to be of inestimable value when, in 1935, he became Manager of the Company's far-sighted venture, the Installation and Flight Test Establishment at Hucknall in Nottinghamshire. He took over from Cyril Lovesey, who was in charge for the first few months only, and inherited two hangars, three aircraft and no more than fifteen people.

Cast in the same mould as Hives he thrived on hard work and during this early period was not averse to staying back into the late hours and with sleeves rolled up help to prepare an installation, or whatever, with others who were just as enthusiastic. He had little time for anyone who didn't pull their weight and could be the proverbial martinet when faced with those who gave him less than he expected of them.

By 1939 the learning curve of aero-engine installation design was still rising very steeply and by the time war was declared Hucknall was firmly established and brimming with talent covering all aspects of the art. The nation had good cause to be grateful for Hucknall's existence as events were to quickly prove. It was here that a great many of the advances and improvements in aviation saw the light of day commencing with marked increases in the performance of such aircraft as the Spitfire. The Airborne Interception radar for "Cat's Eyes" Cunningham's aircraft was assembled there (in a room over a cake shop in Hucknall's High Street actually). In conjunction with the nearby Ilkeston factory a production line of powerplants for Beaufighter, Wellington and Lancaster aircraft was set up. Power-plant installations for a number of prototype aircraft were designed and manufactured, the first being for the Boulton Paul Defiant.

As if this were not enough Dorey took on the responsibility of repairing Hurricanes throughout the Battle of Britain period and at the same time converted 100 of them to Mark II configuration with the much improved Merlin XX engine. As soon as that job was finished he took on the task of producing the first Spitfire IX production aircraft by converting existing Mark V airframes thus relieving Supermarine of the need to stop production to change over to the new model. And all the time, as it had been from the beginning, the relentless efforts for improvement carried on. Better radiators and oil coolers along with their improved aerodynamic installation, better exhaust systems giving increased power or flame-damping properties, more range by improved engine handling, interconnection of controls making the pilot's lot much easier, countless hours of endurance flying to ensure the bomber crews had reliable engines for their long journeys, and so on, and so on. All this entailed an enlargement of facilities. Six new hangars were built and the workforce, which numbered 400 in 1939, was greatly increased, though it never exceeded 1700 during the war years. From 1943 Hucknall was into the jet scene and the whole cycle started again.

By the end of the war its reputation had made it the envy of the aviation world and a jewel in the Rolls-Royce crown. Its uniqueness lay in its autonomy and no other engine manufacturer had a comparable establishment on such a comprehensive scale. If I have wandered somewhat from the biography of Ray Dorey I offer no apology. His name was synonymous with that of Hucknall and for his efforts he was awarded the OBE in 1948. Test pilot John Grierson once remarked that no other aeronautical establishment, with the exception of Farnborough, did as much as Hucknall to advance aviation in Britain during the war years.

R W Harker

Dorey left Hucknall in 1948 and returned to Derby to become Development Engineer for Derwent, Nene, Tay, Dart and reheat. Some thought that he would succeed Lord Hives but his was not to be and in 1951 he moved to Crewe to become Manager of the Motor Car Division. He retired in 1968 and died in 1977.

Ronnie Harker, seen here in 1942, joined Rolls-Royce as a premium apprentice in 1925, serving most of his time on motor cars. His passion for aviation was aroused two years later when his father, who was the Chief Medical Officer of Tyneports, took him to the Hendon Air Pageant where he witnessed the latest in British aircraft designs. No matter how wild his dreams might have been following the experience he could never have imagined that within the short space of ten years

139

he would have learned to fly, joined the Auxiliary Air Force, become a test pilot for Rolls-Royce and, perhaps the crowning glory, taken part in the 1937 Hendon Air Pageant.

With the steady build-up of Hucknall he soon found himself flying the latest and fastest of aircraft and with the outbreak of war he formed a Service liaison team whose job it was to visit the squadrons operating Rolls-Royce powered aircraft and to gain experience of and provide solutions to the many problems being encountered. They also gave instruction on the latest engine handling techniques. During the course of this work he made many friends, some of whom were later to attain high status within the RAF and whose paths he was to cross some years later when he was resident in the London office.

At Conduit Street he was groomed to succeed Willoughby Lappin as the Company's contact with the Services and Ministries and did so with distinction up until his retirement in 1971 when he became an independent aviation consultant. In 1964 he was awarded the OBE for his services to military aviation.

J S Hart (right)

Stan Hart CEng, FRAeS, joined Rolls-Royce at Hucknall in 1938 from Short's at Rochester where he had been a draughtsman working on flying boat and Stirling designs. Born in Wolverhampton he served his apprenticeship with the

140

AJS motorcycle company before moving to the Bendix brake company and later Leyland motors. At Hucknall he worked under Chief Designer Cowdrey (soon to go to Napier's to head their installation design department), Bill Horrocks and Colonel Fell before himself becoming head of installation design during the mid-war years.

His long career spanned the Kestrel at one end and the RB211 at the other. In between he was responsible for most of Hucknall's piston, turboprop and pure jet installations from the early war years up to the VC-10 flying test bed, not to mention production power-plants for many post war Rolls-Royce powered commercial aircraft including the RB211 installation for the Lockheed L-1011 TriStar. His team also designed the VTOL installations for the Flying Bedstead and the Sud VJ-101, the latter being a particularly fine example of the installation engineer's art. During his tenure he presided over the industry's finest and most forward team in this essential sphere of aero-engineering. He retired in 1971.

JSH (right) is seen here "at work" looking at the board of designer Norman Swallow along with Bob Edis, head of the Stress Dept. All three worked on the Mustang projects at Hucknall.

E W Hives

Ernest Hives started at Rolls-Royce in 1908, two years after the formation of the Company, when he was 22 years of age. Four years later he was prominent in establishing the infant Experimental Department, still, at that time, solely concerned with motor cars. He had driven his first car in 1900 when he was fourteen years old and three years later joined C S Rolls and Company in London, prior to the honourable gentleman's allegience with Henry Royce which was formalised as Rolls-Royce Limited. It was during this period that he was summonsed for "driving a light locomotive at a speed greater than 12 mph".

In 1916 he was appointed Manager of the Experimental Dept., a position he was to hold for the next twenty years. With the outbreak of the Great War he was deeply involved in the Company's enforced change in engineering priorities - aero-engine design, development and manufacture. In 1920 he was awarded the MBE for his part in this effort. The inter-war years saw him involved in all matters concerning motor car and aero-engine development, the highlight of which was the direction of the development of the R engine for the Schnieder Trophy races, culminating in 1931 with Britain's possession of the Trophy for all time. During this period Rolls-Royce-powered machines had captured the absolute world speed records on land, sea and in the air. In 1936 he was appointed General Works Manager and in the following year he was given a seat on the board.

With the war clouds gathering he introduced a second source of supply for the Merlin engine by persuading the Government to build a new production facility at Crewe and in the following year, 1939, repeated the exercise at Hillington near Glasgow. By 1942 he was convinced that gas turbines were a worthwhile proposition and conducted a deal whereby the Rover car company's establishment at Barnoldswick would be taken over by Rolls-Royce in exchange for the latter's Meteor tank engine factory in Nottingham.

These were the great years for Rolls-Royce and under his leadership it saw that development and production kept pace with the requirements of the Air Ministry and Royal Air Force. In 1943 he was made a Companion of Honour for his services to the country. This Order is limited to 65 recipients only. The post-war years saw him as Managing Director and in 1948 he was awarded the Royal Aeronautical Society's Gold Medal for his work on aero-engine development. Two years later the King conferred a peerage upon him as Lord Hives of Duffield and the same year he was elected Chairman of the Board. On 11 January 1957, after 48 years with the Company and at the age of 71, he finally said goodbye.

This has been but the merest hint of the achievements of *Hs*. Above everything else he will be remembered as one of the greatest of Britain's industrial leaders, who was, as fortune decreed, the right man in the right place at the right time. Never a name on the lips of people not directly associated with Rolls-Royce he was, nevertheless, respected by all those who had the good fortune to come into contact with him, none more so than the workforce itself. A down-to-earth man he was endowed with the faculties of good engineering sense, good judgement, the ear of those influential within his sphere of industry and the ability to inspire others. He never expected from others efforts beyond which he was prepared to exert himself. Sleep was a necessary encumbrance in life, particularly so during the war years, and when he finally closed his eyes, on

14 April 1965, there ended the life of a man of which a Company and a nation would never see the likes again. For a more detailed look at *Hs* and his career it is recommended that readers should acquaint themselves with Book 7 in the Historical Series entitled Rolls-Royce - Hives, the quiet tiger, by Alec Harvey-Bailey.

W Lappin   Capt R Shepherd

Willoughby "Bill" Lappin is a name that features briefly in the many words that have been written about the history of Rolls-Royce. Yet, by rights, it should be held among the other great names, not because he was a brilliant engineer, he wasn't, but because his forte lay in another direction - influence. An Ulsterman by birth he served in the Royal Naval Air Service with armoured cars until 1917 when he joined Rolls-Royce. Told to make himself useful at the London office in Conduit Street he did just that and more for the next forty years.

His title was never more imposing that Personal Assistant to Hives but it allowed him a freedom hardly ever equalled and certainly not exceeded in the aviation industry. His daily dealings were with the heads of the industry, the pilots and with the hierarchy at the Air Ministry. He had great faith in the Company and its products and was tireless in his efforts to ensure that the customer, whether military or civil, received nothing but the best attention no matter what the need.

During his long association with the Royal Air Force he made countless friends and many of whom he had known as junior officers eventually attained

143

the rank of Air Marshal. He was very close to the Air Staff, as was Hives, and enjoyed a special relationship with its Assistant Chief, Sir Wilfrid Freeman. There can be little doubt that these three hit it off together, to the mutual benefit not only of Rolls-Royce and the Royal Air Force but ultimately the nation's air defences. As one Air Marshal once said "he worked for the RAF and was paid by Rolls-Royce".

Throughout his years he built up an atmosphere of trust that was to pay great dividends for the Company when, in later years, he was often consulted by those earlier acquaintances who had by then risen to greater responsibilities within their respective organisations. He was probably the best salesman Rolls-Royce ever had and soldiered on until he was seventy years old before finally retiring in 1958. His eventual successor at Conduit Street was, most fittingly, Ronnie Harker, the man with whom this story commenced. *Lp* died in 1974 at the age of 86

Capt. Ronnie Shepherd started his working life in the gun department of Vickers Ltd and in 1916 volunteered for the Army. In the following year, with a determination to fly, he transferred to the Royal Flying Corps and after training found himself in France flying FE2b aircraft with 102 Squadron. Towards the end of the war he returned to England and flew night operations with 37 Squadron against Zeppelins. After leaving the Service he persevered with civilian life for eighteen months before rejoining. With 56 Sqn he flew Sopwith Snipes and with 25 Sqn, Gloster Grebes. Back in civvies he became Chief Flying Instructor to Phillips and Powis, (later to become Miles Aircraft) leaving after eighteen months to become a CFI with the newly formed National Flying Services with whom he was to control the Nottingham Flying Club branch at Tollerton in Nottinghamshire.

In October 1931 the Installation and Design Dept. of Rolls-Royce commenced rudimentary flying operations at Tollerton (there being no airfields in Derbyshire at that time) and Capt. Shepherd was seconded to do the flying. With the establishment of a permanent organisation at nearby Hucknall aerodrome in December 1934 he soon left Tollerton to take up the position of Chief Test Pilot for Rolls-Royce. (The honour of being the Company's first paid test pilot, though, belongs to Ronnie Harker).

His reign as Chief Test Pilot lasted until his retirement from flying in 1951 though he did return to make the early free-flights of the world's first manned jet-powered VTOL vehicle, the Flying Bedstead. During his test career he made the maiden flights of most of the Company's flying test beds, not only those powered by piston engines, but jets as well. He started his flying days at 60 mph on Farman Longhorns and finished them at 600 mph in Meteors and Canberras. For his services to test flying he was awarded the OBE. He died in 1955.

Sir Wilfrid Freeman KCB DSO MC FRAeS had a long and varied career after joining the Army when he was twenty. In 1913 he transferred to the Royal Flying Corps and served in France and Egypt. In 1919 he received a permanent commission with the rank of Wing Commander and in 1925 commanded the

144

Sir Wilfrid Freeman   E Schmued

Central Flying School. Two years later he was Deputy Director of Operations and Intelligence at the Air Ministry and in 1930 commenced a three year spell as AOC Palestine and Transjordan. From 1933 to 1936 he was Commandant of the Royal Air Force Staff College after which, for the next four years, he was the Air Member for Research and Development. It was, no doubt, during this period that he acquired his great talent of foreseeing the future needs of the Royal Air Force. He was instrumental in guiding and developing Britain's aircraft industry during the RAF expansion programme from 1936 onwards, encouraged, no doubt, by the leaders of the industry itself with whom he had regular contact.

In 1940, with the rank of Air Chief Marshal, he was appointed to the powerful and influential position of Vice Chief of the Air Staff and it was during his tenure in this office that the events related in the first part of this book took place. In 1942 he was awarded the GCB and in the same year became Chief Executive at the Ministry of Aircraft Production, a post he held for the duration of the war and up to his retirement. He was made a baronet in 1945 and died eight years later.

Edgar Schmued was born in Germany and in 1925 emigrated to Brazil where he attempted to interest local capitalists in an aviation venture but failed miserably. He then joined the service department of General Motors in Brazil and in 1930 received his immigration visa for the USA, arriving at Ellis Island

145

in the February of that year. He applied to the General Aviation Manufacturing Corporation, who built Fokker designs under license, as a designer and was set on. Very soon he had persuaded the management to start a preliminary design department and upon its formation he was appointed its head.

North American Aviation was originally a holding company for a number of aviation related concerns and following an interest acquired by General Motors there was a re-organisation in which the name was transferred to a new aircraft manufacturing venture with a plant at Inglewood in California. Among the key personnel transferred was Ed Schmued. Within the new organisation he became free to concentrate on aircraft design.

His name has always been synonymous with the design of the Mustang, but he could not have done all the work. Such ventures are nearly always the joint endeavours of a team. The actual concept of a fighter with an aft-mounted radiator partly buried within the fuselage belongs to J Leland (Lee) Atwood, the Chief Engineer at North American in 1940. By the time the project was given the go-ahead, with an order of 320 complete aircraft from the British Air Purchasing Commission, the Engineering Department had a new head in Raymond Rice with Ed Schmued as Assistant Chief Engineer and chief of the preliminary design group. The supervision of the detail drawings was undertaken by Schmued, Rice and other senior personnel though in all probability Schmued would have done the lion's share of the work. The notable exception was the design of the now famous laminar flow wing. This came from the Aerodynamics Dept. (it was not part of the original concept) headed by L L Waite. It was

Major T Hitchcock Jr

conceived by Edward Horkey who based his design on the latest developments of NACA. The fact remains, though, that credit for the Mustang's design has always gone to Schmued, as revealed in the Ronnie Harker memo at the beginning of this story. In fact, in a letter to the author in 1983 he stated that 'The P-51 was the first airplane I designed'. He died in 1985.

Major Thomas Hitchcock Jr was born in 1900 into a family that loved horses. Like his father before him he was to become a renowned polo player. With the entry of the United States into the First World War he tried to enlist into the Royal Flying Corps but was rejected because of his age. He then applied to the French air service and was accepted, eventually being assigned to the famous

146

Lafayette Escadrille. He was successful in shooting down several German aircraft before he himself was forced down and captured. He escaped, returned to his unit and eventually transferred to the American Air Service. With the entry of America into the Second World War he requested a commission into the Army Air Force and through his good friend from the First World War days, John G Winant, then American Ambassador to Britain, he acquired the post of Assistant Air Attache at the American Embassy in London.

His name has always been associated with the Merlin Mustang and there can be little doubt that he used his influence, in government, it is said, as well as with the military, to by-pass bureaucracy in his efforts to get the Army Air Force interested in the P-51B. Evidence of this in writing is scarce but an idea of the understanding he had of the requirement for such an aircraft can be detected in the following extracts from a briefing he gave to the Assistant Chief of Staff for Intelligence during a visit to Washington towards the end of 1942.

This fighter business in Europe is a little bit like the women's dress business . . the question of styles and fashions keeps changing all the time. When I went to London about seven months ago, the English Fighter Command wouldn't look at anything that wouldn't fly at 28,000 to 30,000 feet and have plenty of speed. Since then the Focke Wulf has come into active participation on the Western Front; and now all the talk you hear is about greater climb and additional acceleration. This is because the Focke Wulf has those capabilities to a very great degree.

The whole story of the English Fighter planes is more a story of engines than it is of the planes themselves. When you talk about engines, you get practically down to the Rolls engine - that is the Rolls Merlin engine. It started out at about 850 h.p. with a critical altitude of around 15,000 feet. This had a cubic displacement of 1650 cubic inches. In 1939 and 1940 they increased the h.p. rating by some 300 or 400 h.p., up to 1200 h.p., but didn't increase the altitude much. In 1942 they came along with Merlin 46 and 47 and boosted the altitude more than they did the h.p.

Now, when I first went over there, I was rather surprised to run into a report that the Mustang, which is our P-51, was 35 miles an hour faster than the Spitfire V at around 15,000 feet. At 25,000 feet it went a few miles an hour faster and was pulling 290 less h.p. That indicated there must be something aerodynamically good about the Mustang. Dr. E.P. Warner, prominent aeronautical engineer in this country, came over to England and made considerable studies as to the aerodynamic quality of fighter planes. He reduced it to co-efficient drag. The Mustang has a very low co-efficient drag as compared to the Spitfire and that is why it goes faster. It has the lowest co-efficient of drag of any plane in that theatre; and the English gave it a very good report and became very enthusiastic about it.

They said, "Now, if we can put a high altitude engine in this plane we will have the answer to a maiden's prayer." So they put a Merlin 61 engine in it; and they have got us to put one into it in this country. Originally they were going to put in the 61 that peaked at 30,000 feet. Then because the Focke Wulf peaks at 21,000 feet (and because the Spitfire is lighter than the Mustang) they decided the thing to do was to let the Spitfires have the high cover, and try and make the Mustang a fighter against the Focke Wulf. They took the Merlin 61 engine and put a different blower ratio on it so as to get the critical altitude at 21,000 feet, and this is the plane which gives about 426 miles an hour at 21,000 feet. Their original thought was to bring it up higher with the 61 version that peaked at 30,000 feet.

The white hope of the English, in order to combat the FW-190, and particularly the Focke Wulf with the fully rated engine (which they are probably up against now) is by putting Merlin 61 into the Mustang. They believe that will be the best fighting plane for the next year or two; and their preliminary tests indicate they are right. There is one bad thing about the Spitfires - they don't have a carburettor that allows them to sustain negative "G". Those planes won't dive particularly fast, and at 450 miles an hour they are not very manouverable laterally in a dive. Fortunately, the Mustang is manouverable at high speed. There is no flutter trouble

147

and it has a rapid rate of roll. That rate of roll we didn't hear about until the Focke Wulf came out.

They found the Focke Wulf would start to the right and all of a sudden it would flick over and go the other way. Now, in the tests made with the Focke Wulf that they have captured, the plane that would come nearest to staying with it on this reverse twist was the Mustang. That steamed them all up; and they are now negotiating to try and build the Mustang in the United Kingdom and equip it with the Merlin engine; and they are doing all they can to try and get us to build more Mustangs for that particular theatre.

The question of surprise attack is quite a problem. They have been trying to work out some kind of rear warning device so as not to have the men surprised so easily. They get up there in the sky and naturally they can't look in every direction at once. They try to swivel their heads around and manouver the planes so they can see behind them. Some thought has been given to trying to devise some kind of rear warning device. There have been various thoughts. One was to put another man in there who did nothing but look backwards. The added weight made it impracticable. (One person had the idea of putting a dog in there to bark. He was serious about it, too!) Anyway, the British have worked it out for night bombing planes a device which is a radio detection finder - it operates from a generator and will warn when a night fighter comes from behind. It is not adaptable to fighter planes.

It is interesting to note that the British proposed that the Americans should have their own Merlin-powered development aircraft, which might explain why their two prototypes were in fact aircraft taken from an RAF production batch.

It was indeed fortuitous that Tommy Hitchcock was who he was and where he was at this pivotal period in the war, having not only the insight to recognise the Mustang's potential but also the aforementioned influence. There is no doubt in the author's mind that some of this enthusiasm at least was a result of his liaison with Rolls-Royce, a company with whose officials he had a personal and fruitful rapport. His death in April 1944 was one of life's tragic ironies in that it happened when he was flying the very aircraft that he had done so much to promote.

Personnel References

One of the longest held traditions of Rolls-Royce was the personnel reference system. This device provided a means whereby everyone who is entitled is given a "reference" in the form of a corruption of their name or their initial. In many cases a reference was preceded by that of the person to whom the latter is responsible, i.e. *Sft/Hkr*, though such combinations are not recorded in the list below. Such a system provided a simple form of address and enabled internal communication to be carried out without the encumbrance of formal rank and title. In some cases people were referred to verbally by their reference, the most well-known example being Hives who was invariably known as "aitch-ess".

Scarce use of this system has been made within the text of this book, it being most prominent as the means of identifying authorship of the many memos reproduced herein. For the sake of completeness the following is a listing of all Rolls-Royce personnel mentioned by reference within the story and their title during the 1942-43 period.

The identity of titles during the war years is a thankless task as written evidence of them is extremely rare. No family tree appears to have been constructed and the titles rarely, if ever, appeared on any document. Engineers were noted for their responsibilities rather than any title and in many cases their responsibilities covered diverse activities. The majority of those shown here are correct; those that cannot be confirmed as accurate do, never-the-less, reflect the person's responsibilities. Odd man out is Ellor whose reference was phonetic and did not employ the first letter of his surname.

Brns	D S Burns	Military Contracts Manager
Chr	W O W Challier	Performance Engineer
Cyr	W T Collyer	Flight Test Engineer
Dor	R N Dorey	General Manager at Hucknall
E	A G Elliott	Chief Engineer
EWS	E W Still (Dr)	Development Engineer
F	L F R Fell (Lt Col)	Power-Plant Engineer
Hkr	R W Harker	Service Liaison and Test Pilot
Hks	W A Horrocks	Design and Stress Engineer, Head of Drawing Office at Hucknall
Hs	E W Hives	Director and General Works Manager
JSH	J S Hart	Assistant Chief Designer, later Assistant Chief Power-Plant Engineer
Lov	A C Lovesey	Development and Research Engineer
Lp	W Lappin	Hive's Personal Assistant
Lr	J E Ellor	Company advisor at Packard, previously Development and Research Engineer
Rg	A J Rowledge	Senior Designer
RTS	R T Shepherd	Chief Test Pilot
Sft	H J Swift	Production Manager
Sg	A F Sidgreaves (Sir)	Managing Director
Wd	H Wood	Head of Crecy Project

CORRIGENDA

Pages 7 and 146. The title British Air Purchasing Commission should read British Purchasing Commission.

Page 27   The likely purpose of Dr Edward P Warner's visit to the UK, and most probably to Rolls-Royce, was in association with transport aircraft, a subject in which he had a particular interest.

Page 122   Figure 10 is missing from the boost pressure scale on the performance graph. Should read, 4, 6, 8, 10, 12, 14, 16, 18 commencing from the vertical line to the left of 4.

INDEX

The items listed in this index can be found in the main text, footnotes (f) and captions (c). Bold numbers denote illustrations. To avoid unnecessary repetition the pagination of such subjects as Hucknall, Mustang, Merlin 65, individual aircraft etc, has been applied only where noteworthy. Items are sometimes mentioned twice on the same page, either in the text, footnotes or picture captions. No distinction is made between the main text and memos.

155

National Advisory Committee for Aeronautics (NACA) *f27 f73*
North American Aviation (NAA) *10 88*
— Mustang - see under separate heading
— for following personalities see separate headings
— Atwood, J L
— Bouchelle, L B
— Horkey, E J
— Kindelberger, J H
— Legarra, P H
— Rice, R H
— Schmued, E
— Wait, L S
— Waite, L L

Oil system *33*
— breather loss investigation *73*
— liquid-cooled oil cooler *66* **90**

Packard *24 27 35*
— V1650-1 (Merlin 28) *14*
    proposal to install in Mustang *64*
— V1650-3 *24 35 36 64 68* **117**
    problems on test at Wright Field *34 37*
    ground running in XP-51B *65*
— V1650-7 *24 f72 c85*
— V1650-9 *88 90*
Peck, Air Vice Marshall R H (A.C.A.S.) *f11*
Performance - method of calibration - see Appendix VI

Quill, J *f84*

Radiators **76 78 79**
— comparison of Mustang installation with British practice *77*
— suitability - see Appendix VI
Rice, R H *88 144*
Rolls-Royce
— Eagle (22) *c92*
— Goshawk *91*
— Griffon - see under separate heading
— Merlin - see under separate heading
— PI-26 Crecy *92* **104 105**
— Nene *98*
— W2B/23 Welland **105**
— W2B/37 Derwent **105**
— personalities - (non-Hucknall) - see under separate headings
— Ellor, J
— Hives, E W
— Lappin, W
Rowe, N E (D.T.D.) *23 25 26* **94**
Royal Aircraft Establishment, Farnborough *98*

Schmued, E *f10 47 84* **145**
— visit to England *47 48* **86** *87*
— biography - see Appendix VII
Shepherd, R T *40 55* **143**
— biography - see Appendix VII